LABORUM
DULCE
LENIMEN
G. SCHIRMER

FALSTAFF

Lyric Comedy in Three Acts

Based on Shakespeare's "The Merry Wives of Windsor"
and passages from "Henry IV"

Music by

Giuseppe Verdi

Libretto by
ARRIGO BOITO

English Version by
WALTER DUCLOUX

ED. 2538

G. SCHIRMER, INC.
New York

45547

Note

G. SCHIRMER, INC.
609 Fifth Avenue
New York 17, N. Y.

FALSTAFF

"He is a man at once young and old, enterprising and fat, a dupe and a wit, harmless and wicked, weak in principle and resolute by constitution, cowardly in appearance and brave in reality, a knave without malice, a liar without deceit, and a knight, a gentleman, and a soldier, without either dignity, decency, or honor. No ridicule can destroy him; he is safe even in defeat and seems to rise, like another Antaeus, with recruited vigor at every fall."

MAURICE MORGANN

Giuseppe Verdi (1813-1901) was born into a period when Italian comic opera, after more than a century of world-wide triumph, was losing its appeal. The failure of his first work, an *opera buffa* called *Un Giorno di Regno (King for a Day)* no doubt helped to guide the young composer in the direction of musical tragedy, and it was there that Verdi achieved his towering stature. In *Otello,* premiered when he was 73 years old, he set himself a monument which is likely to stand for a long time as an unsurpassed masterpiece in the field of musical tragedy.

Yet, as *opera buffa* receded into the past, Verdi realized more and more that opera needs laughter as well as tears. The time-honored symbol of the stage does show one weeping and one laughing mask. Shakespeare, Verdi's idol as a playwright — he called him "papa" — was equally at home in tragedy and in comedy. Times had, of course, changed, and Italian opera could not return to the pratfalls and guffaws of a hundred years ago. But it was time someone re-introduced the smile onto the operatic stage, and who could do that better than that incredible combination of farmer, patriot, businessman, benefactor, and genius called Giuseppe Verdi?

The bulky figure of Sir John Falstaff had occupied Verdi for many years. But other tasks took precedence, and it was not until 1889 that Arrigo Boito, encouraged by the composer, sent the latter a draft of a libretto which immediately won Verdi's approval. Boito, a man of brilliant endowments both as a musician and a man of letters, had already written the libretto to *Otello* and knew what Verdi wanted. Their *Falstaff* is actually an amalgam of the two Shakespearean characters, the finely drawn figure from *King Henry IV* and the sorry caricature of knightliness gone to seed from *The Merry Wives of Windsor.* The plot is that of the latter comedy.

Yet, the Maestro was 76 years old. World-famous, rich, and wise, should he not leave well enough alone? Would he live long enough to finish a task which could not be tossed off in a few months but would take years to complete? With remarkable insight, Boito allayed the old man's fears with a simple statement: "There is only one way to end your life's work more fittingly than with *Otello*. That is to end it with *Falstaff*."

First produced at La Scala on February 9, 1893, *Falstaff* was an immediate success. The title-role was sung by Victor Maurel who also played the part in the first performance in North America, at the Metropolitan Opera House on February 4, 1895. Another notable Metropolitan production occurred in 1909, with Toscanini conducting a brilliant cast headed by Antonio Scotti and Emmy Destinn. Scotti sang the part again in 1925, this time opposite Lucrezia Bori, Beniamino Gigli, and Frances Alda. The part of Ford was entrusted to a newcomer who became an overnight sensation and subsequently was to carry the prestige of the American singer to new heights: Lawrence Tibbett. Since then, Falstaff has won an ever-increasing audience all over America.

W. D.

CAST OF CHARACTERS

SIR JOHN FALSTAFF	Baritone
FENTON, a young gentleman	Tenor
FORD, a wealthy burgher	Baritone
Dr. CAJUS, a physician	Tenor
BARDOLPH } followers of Falstaff	Tenor
PISTOL } followers of Falstaff	Bass
MRS. ALICE FORD	Soprano
ANNE (Nannetta), her daughter	Soprano
MRS. MEG PAGE	Mezzo-Soprano
DAME QUICKLY	Mezzo-Soprano

ROBIN, Falstaff's page

An Innkeeper in Ford's household

Burghers and street-folk; Ford's servants; Maskers as elves, fairies, witches; etc.

PLACE: Windsor

TIME: Reign of King Henry IV

SYNOPSIS OF SCENES

			Page
ACT I	Part 1	Inside the Garter Inn	1
	Part 2	A Garden	47
ACT II	Part 1	At the Garter Inn	127
	Part 2	A room in Ford's house	191
ACT III	Part 1	An open square	291
	Part 2	Windsor Park	331

FALSTAFF

Libretto by
Arrigo Boito
English version by
Walter Ducloux

Music by
Giuseppe Verdi

Act One

Part One

Inside the Garter Inn.

A table. A large armchair. A bench. On the table the remnants of a meal, several bottles, and a goblet. An inkwell with quills, some paper and a lit candle. A broom leaning against the wall.

A main entrance upstage, another door to the left.

Falstaff is busy heating a stick of sealing-wax over the candle and sealing two letters with the help of a ring. This done, he extinguishes the candle and starts drinking, stretched out comfortably in the armchair.

Dr C
FAL
Hai fiac-ca-ta la
You have beat- -en my
-n'al-tra botti--glia di Xe-res.
Bring me some more of this sher-ry!
p
mia giu-men-ta ba-ia, Sfor-za-ta la mia ca-sa.
mare un-til she's dy-ing, you broke in-to my quar-ters.
Ma
But
3
Trop-pa gra-zia! U-na vecchia ci-
Thank you kind-ly! Such an ug-ly old
non la tua mas-sa-ia.
spared your keep-er's cry-ing!
p
pp

Dr C
spo_sa.-
crea-ture!
(1)
ff
Am - - - - pio Mes_
Might- - - - y Sir
mf
Dr C
_se_re, Se fo_ ste ven_ti vol_te John Fal_staff Ca_va_
Moun-tain, if twen - - ty times as no - ble and twen - ty times Sir
p
Dr C
_lie_re Vi for_ze_rò a ri _ spondermi.
Fal-staff, I'd force you yet to an-swer me.
FAL
(lazily)
Ec_ _ co la mia ri_
Well, then, I'll tell you
mf
pp
UN POCO MENO ANIMATO
Dr C
ben legato
E
Go
FAL
_sposta: "Ho fat_to ciò ch'hai det_to.»
loud-ly: " I've done the things you men-tion . . .
UN POCO MENO ANIMATO
p
ppp

Dr C
FAL
(screaming)
poi?
on!
M'appel_le_rò al Con_si_glio Re_
I shall ap-peal to the Court of the
L'ho fat_to ap_ _ _po_sta.
and done them proud-ly.
_al.
King.
Vat_ti con Di_o. Sta zit_to o a_vrai le
Heav-en may keep you! The joke will be on
(turning his fury on Bardolph)
Non è fi_
Now a-bout
bef_fe; quest'è il con_si_glio mi_o.
you, Sir. Take it from me, John Fal staff!"

COME PRIMA
Dr. C.
-ni - ta!!
this one!
Bar-
You
FAL
Al dia - vo - lo!
To hell with you!
COME PRIMA
(2)
ff
Dr. C
-dol - fo!
ras - cal!
Tu, ier, m'hai fat - to
Last night you set me
BAR.
Ser Dot - to - re.
Hon - ored doc - tor!
mf
Dr. C
be - re.
drink - ing.
B
Pur troppo! e che dolo - re!
In-deed, Sir! I still am pay - ing
3

(inviting Cajus to feel his pulse)
B
Sto mal.
the bill!
D'un tuo pro_no_sti_co m'as_
I need your help, my dear phy-
B
_si_sti.
-si-cian.
f
Ho l'inte_sti _ no guasto.
Have I a shrunk-en liv-er?
marcato
Malan_no a
This blast-ed
B
_gl'o - sti che dan la çal_ce al vi_no!
host must have thinned his wine with poi-son!
f
pp
Dr. C.
La ve_do.
I see it.
(pointing to his own nose)
B
Ve - di que - sta me_teo_ra?
See what shines here so bright-ly!

B
Es - sa si cor ca ros - sa co-sì o - gni
Fi - ery and red, it glows like a star in the
pp
Dr. C.
(furious)
Pro - no-sti - co di for - ca!
A light by which to hang you!
M'hai fat - to
You made me
B
not-te.
dark-ness.
ff
mf
mf
(pointing to Pistol)
Dr. C
ber, furfan - te, con lui, nar - ran - - do
drunk, you ras - cal, while he was tell - - - ing
Dr. C
fra - sche;
sto - ries.
Poi, quan - do fui ben
Then, when my mind was
mf

Dr C

ciùschero, m'hai vuo - ta - te le tasche. Chi
deaf and numb, you took all I had on me. *(with dignity)* Who

Non io.
Not I!

f

Dr C

fu?
FAL. then?

(addressing Pistol)

Pi - sto - la! *(approaching*
You, Pis - tol! *Falstaff)*

PISTOLA

Pa -
My

(3)

ff

legatiss.

pp

(advancing on Pistol)

Dr C

Cer - to fu
Yes, it was

(still stretching lazily in his chair)

FAL

Hai tu vuo - ta - te le tasche a quel Mes - se - re?
Have you di - vest - ed this man of his be - long - ings?

P

- dro - ne.
mas - ter?

Dr. C
lui. Guar - da - te
he! Be - hold him!
ff
p
Dr. C
co - me s'atteg - gia al nie - go quel
Read what his snout is tell - ing al -
Dr. C
cef - fo da bu - giar - do! Qui c'e - ran due scel -
- though he would de - ny it! I know that I had
p
(turning his pockets inside out)
Dr. C
- li - ni del re - gno d'E - do - ar - do e sei mezze - co -
on me two good Ed - ward - ian shil - lings and six flor - ins of

Dr C
-ro-ne. Non............ ne ri-man più se-gno.
sil - ver. Noth - - - ing is left, so help me!
(solemnly brandishing the broom)
PIS.
Pa-dron, chie-do di
Sir John, al - low me
f
f
P
(to Dr. Cajus, with intent)
bat-ter-mi con quest'ar-ma di le-gno.
kind-ly now to sweep him off the prem-is-es!
Vi smen-
You're a
(4)
ff
Dr C.
Bi - fol-co! tu parli a un gen-ti-
You block-head! Of-fend a man of
P
-ti-sco!
li - ar!
mf
ff

Dr. C
-luo-mo!
sta-tion!
Pez-zen-te!
You beg-gar!
Can!
Dog!
P
Gon-zo!
Stu-pid!
Be-stia!
Var-let!
mf
ff
Spau-racchio!
You scare-crow!
Ger-mo-glio di man-
You fee-ble-mind-ed
Vil!
Lout!
Gnomo!
Pix-y!
-dràgora!
id-i-ot!
Tu.
You!
Sì.
Yes.
(motioning Pistol to hold back)
FAL.
Ehi
Wait!
(attacking Dr. Cajus)
Chi?
Who?
Ri-pe-ti!
You mean it?
Sa-et-te!!!
I'll show you!

FAL
là! Pi - sto - la! Non sca - ricar - ti
Wait! You hot - head! This is no place to
dim.
p
(to Bardolph)
FAL
qui. Bar - dol - fo! Chi ha vuo - ta - te le tasche a quel Mes-
fight. Hey Bar-dolph! Who has emp-tied the pock-ets of the
p
Dr. C.
marcato
(quickly)
ANCORA POCO MENO
Fu l'un dei du - e.
I'm sure they both did!
BAR.
(serenely pointing to Dr. Cajus)
Co - stui be - ve, poi pel gran
He was drink-ing, heav - i - ly
FAL
- se - re?
doc - tor?
(5)
ANCORA POCO MENO
ppp calmo

B
be - re Perde i suoi cin-que sen - si, poi ti narra u-na
drink - ing, Till he had lost his sens - es. Now he tells you a
8
B
fa - vola Ch'egli ha so - gna - to mentre dor - mi sotto la
fair - y-tale, some fan - cy fa - ble, No doubt dreamed up while under the
B
ta-vo-la.
ta - ble.
MENO MOSSO
(to Dr. Cajus)
FAL.
L'o - di? Se ti ca - pa - ci - ti, del ver.......... tu sei si -
Well now . . . this man's ve - rac - i - ty can - not in faith be
MENO MOSSO

FAL
-cu - ro. I fat - ti son ne - ga - ti. Vattene in pa -
doubt-ed. Your state-ments stand re - fut - ed. I bid you leave in
p
3
Dr. C.
Giu - ro che se mai m'ubri - a-co anco - ra all'o-ste -
Hear me! If I drink once a - gain and low - er my de -
FAL
-ce.
peace.
f
Dr. C
-ri - a Sa - rà fra gen - te o - ne - sta,
-fenc - es 'Twill be with men of worth and
f
COME PRIMA
Dr. C
so - bria, ci - vi - - - - - - le e
hon - or who pay their ex -
COME PRIMA
(6)
f

Dr C
pi
-pens
pp
(Exits through the door at the left.)
Dr C
-a.
BAR.
-es!
A
A
(escorting the Doctor to the door, grotesquely chanting)
PIS.
A
A
B
men.
FAL.
men!
3
Ces-si l'an - ti-fo-na. Laur-la-te in contrat-
Cease your an - tiph-o-nals! Your coun-ter-point is
P
men.
men!
p

PRESTO
PIÙ LENTO
(meaningfully)
FAL
_tempo.
dread-ful.
PRESTO
L' ar_te sta in que_sta
Theft has its laws of
ff
PIÙ LENTO
legato
mas_sima:
art-ist-ry:
ppp
«Ru_bar con gar - bo e a tem - po.»
" To steal with charm and good tim - ing!"
pp
legato
f
ALL°. COME PRIMA
(contemptuously)
(shushing them)
ff
Siete dei roz_zi ar_ti_sti.
Lu-di-crous pair of art-ists!
Sss.
Sss.
BAR.
A
A
PIS.
A
A
ALL°. COME PRIMA
f

(He starts examining the bill which the innkeeper has brought along with the bottle of sherry.)
FAL
mf
f
(7)
senza misura
p
fp
6 pol - li:
Six pul - lets:
6 scelli - ni.
six_ shil - lings.
30 giarre di Xe - res:
Thir - ty flag - ons of sher - ry:
(to Bardolph, throwing him his purse,
più forte
2 li - re.
Two flor - ins.
3 tacchi - ni...
Three par - trid - ges . . .
Fru - ga nel - la mia bor - sa.-
See how much I have left here!
ALLEGRO ♩ = 100
then slowly reading on)
2 fa - gia - ni.
Brace of pheas - ants . . .
Un' ac -
one an -
pp

FAL
-ciu - - - - - ga.
BAR. cho - - - - vy!
(taking coins out of the purse and putting them on the table)
Fruga. - Fruga.
Go on! Non-sense!
Un mark, un mark, un penny. Ho frugato.
A shil-ling, a shil-ling, a pen-ny. This is all, Sir.
a tempo
pp
f
FAL.
(rising)
Sei la mia di - stru-
Ah, you lout, you de -
BAR. (throwing the purse on the table)
Qui non c'è più uno spicciolo.
See . . . there is not a pen-ny left!
FAL
-zio - ne! Spendo ogni set-te gior-ni die-ci ghi-ne-e! Be-
-stroy me! Week af-ter week I spend ten guin-eas to in-dulge you, you
mf
p
ff

FAL
- o - ne!
drunk - ard!
p
allarg. un poco
MODERATO ♩= 80
legato
So che se andiam, la not - - te, di ta - ver - - na in ta -
Night af - ter night I pon - - der, As from inn to inn we
MODERATO ♩= 80
ppp legato
- ver - - - - na Quel tuo na - so ar - den -
wan - - - - - der, How your mon - strous nose can
string.
- tis - si - mo mi ser - ve da lanter - - na; Ma quel risparmio
yield the glow To guide me here and yon - - der. But what I save on
tr
string. poco a poco

string. sempre poco a poco

FAL

d'o-lio tu lo consumi in vi-no. Son tren-t'an-ni che ab-
lamp-oil You waste on drink and din-ing. So for thir-ty long

string. sempre poco a poco

mf *ff* *ff*

(*to Bardolph*)

FAL

-be-ve-ro quel fun-go por-po-ri-no! Co-sti
years I keep Your fi-ery nose a-shin-ing! You're too

mf

PIÙ MOSSO 𝅗𝅥 = 132 (*to Pistol*) (*shouting*)

FAL

troppo.... E tu pu-re. O-ste! un'altra bot-
cost-ly. And you al-so. Ho there! A flag-on of

PIÙ MOSSO 𝅗𝅥 = 132

f *ff*

FAL

-ti-glia.
sher-ry!

ff

(to Bardolph and Pistol)
FAL
Mi strug - ge - te le car - ni.
You are threat - 'ning my sub-stance.
(8)
f
dim.
pp
FAL
Se Fal-staff s'as-sot - ti - glia
A weak and slen - der Fal - staff
ppp
FAL
Non è più lui, nessun più
Is not him - self! A fear - some
FAL
l'a - ma; in que - st'ad -
night - mare! For in this
marcato

PIÙ LENTO ♩= 92
Maestoso
FAL
do - me.. C'è un miglia - - io di
paunch here you will find all the
PIÙ LENTO ♩= 92
f Maestoso
FAL
lin - gue che an_nun - ciano il mio no_me!
rea - sons for my im-mor - tal glo - ry. (assenting)
PIS.
Fal - staff im-
Fal - staff the
(looking at himself and patting his paunch)
FAL
Que _ st'è il mio
This roy - al
BAR.
(assenting)
E_nor - - me Fal_staff!
Tre-men - - dous Fal_staff!
P
-men - so!
Might - y!

FAL
re - - - - - - - gno. Lo in-gran - - - di-
treas- - - - - - ure, I'll make it
ff
pp cres.
FAL
BAR.
rò.
grow!
Im-men - - so Fal - - - - - -
Tre-men - - - dous Fal - - - - - -
PIS.
E-nor - - me Fal - - - - - - -
Tre-men- - dous Fal - - - - - - -
ff
FAL
Ma è tem-po d'assot-tigliar l'in-ge-gno...
The mind, though, no longer yields to mat-ter!
B
-staff!
-staff!
As-sot-ti-
Then let us
P
-staff!
-staff!
As-sot-ti-
Then let us
p

LO STESSO TEMPO
(all three in a huddle)
AL
B
P
V'è no_to un tal, qui del pa_
There-lives—in—town—a—cer—tain
_gliam.
think!
_gliam.
think!
(9) LO STESSO TEMPO
pp
_e_ _se ch'ha no_ _me Ford?
gen-tle-man whose name is Ford.
Sì.
Yes.
Sì.
Yes.
Quel_l'uom è un gran_bor_ _ghe_ _se...
A man of wealth and of dis_ _tinc_ _tion.
Più li_be_ral d'un
Most wealth-y and most

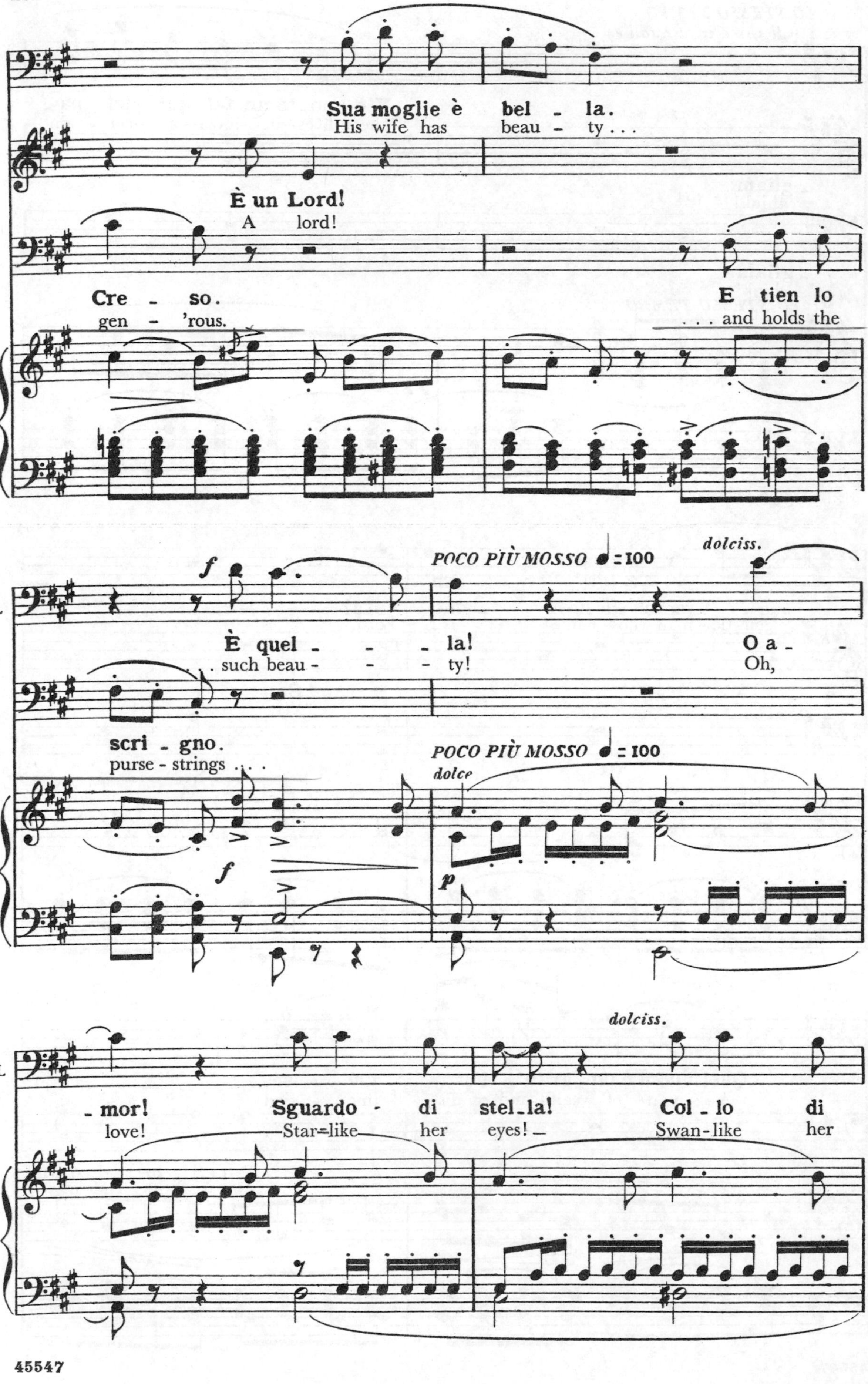

FAL

Sua moglie è bel - la.
His wife has beau - ty . . .

B

È un Lord!
A lord!

P

Cre - so.
gen - 'rous.

E tien lo
. . and holds the

f

POCO PIÙ MOSSO ♩ = 100

dolciss.

FAL

È quel - - la!
. such beau - - ty!

O a -
Oh,

P

scri - gno.
purse - strings . . .

POCO PIÙ MOSSO ♩ = 100

dolce

f

p

FAL
ci_gno! e il lab_bro?! un fior! Un fior che
bos-om! Like blos-soms her ros - - y lips be -
FAL
ri - - - - - - de. A _ li_ce è il
- guil - - - - - - ing! Her name is
legg.
m.s.
FAL
no_me, e un gior - no co_me passar mi
A - lice. One morn - ing she saw me from her
p dolce con espress.
3
FAL
vi - de ne' suoi pa - rag - gi... ri - se... M'ar_
win - dow, and I be - held her smil - ing! Then
dolciss.
ff
3
pp

POCO PIÙ MOSSO ♩= 112
FAL
- de - a l'estro ama-to-rio nel cor. La
light -, ning struck in the deep of my heart. Di -
(10)
POCO PIU MOSSO ♩= 112
f
mf
Dea vi - bra - va rag-gi di specchio u-sto - rio su
-vine, her ra - diant eyes turned their brilliant and blind - ing light — on
me, su me, sul fian - co
me, on me! On chest and
più calmo
(strutting)
bal-do, sul gran to - ra-ce, Sul ma - schio piè, sul fu - sto
shoul-ders, on legs like boul-ders, This paunch so proud, this man - ly

dolciss.
♩= 100
saldo, er - to, ca - pa - ce; E il suo de - sir in
stat-ure, no - ble, im - pos - ing. And then her glance, a -
p
lei ful - ge - a sì al mio con - giun - to Che pa - re - a
-glow with wild de - sire, would plain - ly tell me what I hoped to
(in falsetto)
dir: Io son di Sir John Fal - - - staff E a
BAR.
hear: "I love you, Sir John Fal - - - staff!" Yet,
f
(11)
Pun - to.
Un - quote!

FAL
ca - po.-
hear me:
U - n'al - tra;
There's some-one . .
B
u - n'al - tra!
An - oth - er?
PIS
u -
An-
ppp leggere e staccate molto
FAL
E questa ha no - me: Mar-ghe - ri - ta.
. . her-name, - it - seems, is - Mis - tress - Page.
f
P
- n'al - tra!
- oth - er?
La chia - - man
They call her
FAL
È an - ch'es - sa de' miei pre - gi in - va -
For her, too, I hold a fa - tal fas - ci -
P
Meg.
Meg.

L

BAR. -ghi - ta. E anch'essa tien le chia-vi del-lo scri - - -
- na - tion, and dar-ling Meg is mis-tress. . of the purse- - - -

marcate

del-lo scri - - -
. . . of the purse- - -

marcate

del-lo scri - - -
. . . of the purse- - -

-gno. Co - sto - - - ro sa-
-strings! These beau - - - ties on

-gno.
-strings!

-gno.
-strings!

f

-ran le mie Gol-con-de e le mie Co - - - - - - ste
wings of gold shall take Sir John to El - - - - - - do-

p

(letting himself be admired)
FAL
d'o - - - ro! Guar-
- ra - - - do. Be -
p
cres.
- da - te. Io sono an - co-ra u-na pia-cen-te e - sta - te di San Mar -
- hold me! I shall yet be the knight in shin - ing ar - mor who will re -
mezza voce
- ti - - - - - - - no. A voi, due let-tere infuo -
- deem you! And you shall ex-pe-dite the
pp
(handing Bardolph one of the two letters on the table)
PIÙ ANIMATO
REC.vo
Presto
- ca - - te. Tu por - ta que-sta a
(12) mat - - ter: This let - ter bring to
PIÙ ANIMATO
f
REC.vo

(Bardolph takes the letter.)
Meg; ten_tiam la sua vir_tù. Già ve_do che il tuo
Meg. Her vir-tue shall be tried! I see: Your fi-ery
na_so ar_de di ze_lo.
nose glows at the pros_pect.
(to Pistol, tending him the other letter)
E tu por_ta que_sta ad A li_ce.
And you, you bring this one to A_lice!
PIS.
(refusing with dignity)
Por_to u_na spa_da al fian_co. Non sono un Messer Pan_darus. Ri_
No! By my sword, I shall not! A low and shame-ful go-be-tween? No,

MENO ANIMATO
FAL.
(with calm contempt)
Saltim - banco.
Ah, you wind-bag!
BAR.
(stepping forth and depositing the letter on the table)
Sir John in que - st'in-
Sir John, in this en -
P
- cuso.
nev-er!
(13) MENO ANIMATO
pp molto staccato
(interrupting him)
FAL
Chi?
. . . what?
B.
-tri-go non posso accondi - scendervi.
-deav-or you must pro-ceed with-out me.
Lo vie - ta...
I'm bound by . . .
L'O-
. . . my
ALL°. PRESTO ♩=132
(noticing the page, Robin, just entering the door)
(turns to Bardolph and Pistol)
FAL
Ehi!
Hey,
pag-gio!
Rob-in!
An - da - te a im -
Get out and
B
- no - re!
hon - or.
ALL°. PRESTO ♩=132
p

FAL
(to the Page)
-pendervi
hang your-selves . . .
Ma non più a me.-
but not on me!
Due
These
let-te-re, pren-di, per due si-gno-re.
let-ters here, take them to two young la-dies.
f
Con-se-gna tosto, corri, via, lesto, va!- lesto,
Go, take them quick-ly, hur-ry, go! Quick-ly! Fly, scur-ry,
fp
cres.
(The Page hurries off.) (to Pistol and Bardolph)
va, va, va, va, va!
go, go, go, go, go!
L'O-
Your
(14)
ff

ALL.º SOSTENUTO
FAL
♩= 112
_no - re! La - dri! Voi sta_te
hon - or? Scoun - drels! You dare to
li_gi all'onor vo_stro, voi!.. Clo - a - - che d'igno_
speak to me of hon - or? You? You foul and filth-y
_mi - nia, quan - - do, non sempre, noi.................. Possiam star
mon - grels. . When on oc - ca - sion we may find our
MENO MOSSO ♩=100
li - gi al nostro. Io stesso, sì, i_o, i_o, De_vo talor da un
own in per-il? Yes, I, Sirs. I. . . lis ten: I have had to hide my

FAL
la - to porre il timor di Di - o E, per neces - si -
glanc - es, ask - ing the grace of Heav - en, as in the throes of
- tà, svi - ar l'o - no - - - -
need I pawned my hon - - -
leggeriss.
- - - re, u - - sa - re stra - ta - gem - mi ed e -
- - - or, sought ref - uge - in - some - guile - or - some de -
p
- quivo - ci, destreggiar, bordeg - gia - re. E
- cep - tion, in a ruse or a false - hood. And

pp
FAL
voi,.. coi vo_stri
you, de - crep - it
pp
f
FAL
cen - ci e col_l'oc_chia - - ta
wretch - es, you stink-ing, vile hy - -
fp e molto stacc.
FAL
tòr - ta da gat - to par - - do e i
-e - nas, who feed on car - - rion, you
FAL
fe - - ti_di sghi_gnaz - zi a_ve_te a
pu - - tre-fied rap - scal - lions, You speak of

FAL
scor - ta il vo - stro Onor! Che o - no - re?! che o -
hon - or... and this to me? What hon - or? Speak
f
FAL
- nor? che o - nor! che cian - cia! che ba - ja!
up! Come on, you id - iots, you ass - es!
FAL
f
tr
tr
tr
ff
(in a ponderous tone)
MENO MOSSO
legato
FAL
f
(15)
Può l'o - no - re.......... ri - em - pir - vi la
MENO MOSSO
Can your hon - or——— fill your paunch when it's

FAL
pan_cia? No. - Può l'o _ nor ri_met _ tervi u_no
emp - ty? No! Or can hon - or cure — a brok - en
pp
FAL
stin_co?- Non può. Nè un pie_de?- No. - Nè un di _ to?- No. - Nè un ca_
an - kle? Oh no! A fin-ger? No. A toe-nail? No! Or a
FAL
_pel_lo?- No! - L'onor non è chi_
whisk-er? No. For hon-or is no
ppp
FAL
_rur _ go. - Che è dunque?- U _ na pa_
sur - geon. What is it? On - ly a
f
p

POCO PIÙ MOSSO
FAL
-ro-la.
word!
Che c'è in questa pa-
This word, what is it
ALL°. AGITATO ♩= 120
leggeriss.
-ro - la?-
real - ly?
C'è del-l'a-ria che
Just a breeze that will
vo - la.
van - ish.
Bel co-
Fan - cy
-strutto!
fic-tion!
a mezza voce
L'o-
A

COME PRIMA
FAL
-no - re lo può sen-tir chi è mor-to? No.- Vi - ve sol coi
dead man, can he take pride-in hon-or? No! Yet he who is
COME PRIMA
pp
FAL
vi - vi?... Nep - pu - re: per - chè a
liv - ing? Not eith - er. For he who
PIÙ MOSSO ♩= 126
p
PIÙ MOSSO ♩= 126
pp
legg. e stacc.
pp
a mezza voce
FAL
tor - to Lo gon-fian le lu-sin-ghe, lo corrom - pe l'or-
owns it has no way to de-fend it. It is frail and will
FAL
-go-glio, L'ammor - ban le ca-lun-nie;
crum-ble, killed off by hu-man weak-ness.
f

POCO PIÙ MOSSO
AL
e per me non ne vo_glio, no! non ne
There-fore I do not want it, no, do not
POCO PIÙ MOSSO
(16)
FAL
voglio, no,.. no, no!
want it, no! Ah, no!
FAL.
Ma, per tornare a voi, fur_fanti, ho atteso troppo, E vi di_
But to re-turn to you, you scoun-drels: I've been too le-nient. I now dis-

(He grabs the broom and chases Bardolph and Pistol around the room. They try to hide behind the table.)
FAL
scac_cio.
-miss you.
O_là!
A-way!
(17)
mf
FAL
Le_sti!
Quick-ly,
Le_sti!
scur - ry!
al ga_lop_po! al ga_
I shall teach you how to
FAL
_lop_po!
hur - ry.
Il ca_pe - stro assai be - ne vi
From the gal - lows you'll soon swing and

FAL
sta. Le-sti, le-sti, le-sti, al ga-lop-po,al ga-
sway. Hur-ry, quick-ly, hur-ry! On your way! Bet-ter
FAL
-lop-po! La-dri! la-dri! la-dri!
hur-ry! Rob-bers, scoun-drels, ras-cals,
ff
FAL
la-dri! Via di qua, via di qua! via di qua! via di
ban-dits! If you stay you will pay. On your way! On your

(*Bardolph flees through the door at the left, Pistol through the center after having received some blows. Falstaff follows Pistol out the door.*)

Act One

Part Two

A Garden. To the left Ford's house. A group of trees center-stage. Alice, Ann, Meg, Mrs. Quickly, later Ford, Fenton, Dr. Cajus, Bardolph, and Pistol.

(*Meg and Mrs. Quickly enter from the right and cross towards Ford's house on whose threshold they encounter Alice and Ann just leaving the house.*)

(still speaking to Meg)
A
Giungi in buon
Now let me
(patting Ann's cheek)
Q
Botton di ro - - sa!
My Ann, my rose - - bud!
A
punto.
tell you:
M'acca - de un fat - to da tra - se - co-
I am a - mazed at some - thing that oc-
p
(to Meg)
A
-lar.
-curred.
Narra il tuo
Speak out and
NAN.
(coming closer, too)
Che co - sa?
What is it?
MEG.
An - che a me.
So am I.
(having conversed with Ann, now approaching inquisitively)
QUIC.
Che?
What?

A
N
M
Q
(mysteriously)
ca_so.
tell me!
Pro_mes - sa.........
But prom - ise:
Nar_ra, nar_ra.
Tell us, tell us!
Nar_ra il tu_o.
No, I lis-ten.
Nar_ra, nar_ra.
Tell us, tell us!
pp
pp
.... di non ciar - lar.
No word of this!
Ti pa - - re?!
Of course not!
Oi -
Oh

A
Q
-bò!......... Vi pa - re?!
no! Of course not!
(20)
Dun - que:
Hear then:
se m'ac - - - con-cias - si
If I were will - ing
a entrar nei rei pro - po si-ti del diavo-lo, sa-
to make a naugh - ty bar-gain With the Dev - il, my
-rei......... pro - mos - sa al gra - - do di Ca-val - le-
sin would be re - ward - - ed with the rank of

A
-res - - -sa!
MEG. La - - dy!
Motteggi.
You're jok-ing!
(searching her pocket for a letter)
An-ch'io.
Mine al-so!
Non più pa - ro - - -
Why go on talk - - -
(produces the letter)
M
-le Chè qui sciu-pia - mo la lu - ce del so-le.
-ing when we can call on the sun - light to help us?
stacc.
pp
ALI.
(searching her pocket)
An - ch'i-o.
I al-so.
NAN.
Oh!!
Oh?
M
Ho u-na let-te-ra.
I have a let - ter.
QUIC.
Oh!!
Oh?
f

(gives her letter to Meg.)
A
Leggi.
Read it!
(exchanging her own letter with that of Alice)
M
Leggi.
Read it!
ppp
(reading Alice's letter)
AND.te SOSTENUTO ♪= 126
M
Fulgida A_li_ce! a_mor t'offro... Ma
"Ex-qui-site A-lice! I a-dore you."... What
(21)
AND.te SOSTENUTO ♪= 126
p
3
ALLEGRO ♩= 126
Lo stesso movimento
M
come?! Che cosa dice?
is this? I can't be-lieve it.
Salvo che il nome la frase è u_guale.
But for the name the words are the same.
ALLEGRO ♩= 126
Lo stesso movimento
p
6
8

Come Prima
ALI.
(her eyes on the letter in her hand, repeats the contents of Meg's letter)
ALL.º come prima
Ful-gi-da Meg! a-mor t'offro...
"Ex-qui-site Meg! I a-dore you. . . ."
Qua
Here
M
(reading the letter in her hand)
a-mor bra-mo.
"I im - plore you . . ."
Come Prima
ALL.º come prima
p
A
AND.te come prima
Meg, là A - li - ce.
"Meg", there "A-lice"!
M
È tal e quale.
Letter for let-ter!
AND.te come prima
p
A
t'a - mo.
love you!"
M
non domandar per-chè, ma dim - mi:
"Ah, do not ask me why, but say. . . I
pp

ALL.º come prima
A
Pur non gli offer - si ca - gion.
I can-not see what this means.
M
Il nostro ca - so è pur strano.
I find it all most con - fus-ing.
QUIC.
Guardiam con
Let's not be
ALL.º come prima
(22)
(All in the group crowd around the letters, perusing them and fingering them with great interest.)
M
Gli stessi
The same ex-
Q
flem - - - - ma.
hast - - - - y!
ALI.
Lo stesso in - chio - stro.
A - like the writ - ing!
NAN.
Lo stesso
Ev-ery-thing
M
ver - si.
- pres-sions!
Q
La stessa ma - no.
E - ven the pa - per.

AND.te come prima
(reading jointly, each her own letter)
A
...sei la ga_ia co_
"You are cheer-ful and
N
stem_ma.
match-es.
M
...sei la ga_ia co_
"You are cheer-ful and
p
A
_ma_re, il com_par ga_ _io son i_ _o, e fra noi
charm-ing, I deb-o-nair and dis-arm-ing: We are a
M
_ma_re, il com_par ga_ _io son i_ _o, e fra noi
charm-ing, I deb-o-nair and dis-arm-ing: We are a
ALL.o come prima
A
NAN. due.... fac_ciamo il pa_ _io. Già.
pair joined by our for- -tune." Well!
Lui, lei, te.
She...you...he...
M
QUIC. due.... fac_ciamo il pa_ _io.
pair joined by our for- -tune."
Un paio in
...a pair of
ALL.o come prima
p

Sempre lo stesso movimento
A
Faccia - mo il pa - io...................... in un amor ri -
" . . . in love u - nit - - ed, a pair of doves so
Q
tre.
three!
Sempre lo stesso movimento
pp
(all reading the letters)
- den - - te di don - - na
ten - - - der, the fair - - est
(exaggeratedly)
dolciss.
bel - - la e d'uom ap - pa - ri - scen - te e il vi - so
NAN.
la - - dy . . . a man of weight and splen - dor!" "Your radiant
ap - pa - ri - scen - te.
MEG.
" . . . of weight and splen - dor!"
ap - pa - ri - scen - te.
QUIC.
" . . . of weight and splen - dor!"
ap - pa - ri - scen - te.
" . . . of weight and splen - dor!"
pp

A
tu - o su me ri-splen-de - rà co - me u-na
beau - ty on me will shed its light, As bright and
stel - - la co-me u-na stel - la sul - l'im-men - si
smil - - ing out of the sky — A star — will shine at —
ALL.o più presto
(laughing)
-tà. Ah! ah! ah! ah! ah! ah! ah! ah! ah! ah! ah! ah! ah! ah! ah!
NAN.
night." Ha, ha, ha, ha, ha, ha, ha, ha, ha, ha, ha, ha, ha, ha, ha,
MEG.
QUIC.
ALL.o più presto

senza misura
parlato (spoken)
A
ah! Ri_spon_di al tuo scu_die_re, John Falstaff Ca_va_lie_re.
ha! "Re-ply to your ad-mir-er! Your serv-ant, Sir John Fal-staff."
N
ah!
ha!
M
ah!
ha!
Q
ah!
ha!
col canto
ALLEGRO ♩= 120
f
Mostro!
Mon-ster!
Mostro! Mostro!
Mon-ster, mon-ster!
Mostro! Mostro!
Mon-ster, mon-ster!
Mostro! Mostro!
Mon-ster, mon-ster!
ALLEGRO ♩= 120
(23)
leggero
pp

A
N
M
Q
Dobbiam gab - bar-lo.
We must de - fy him . . .
E
. . . We'll
E far-ne chiasso.
. . . and twit and taunt him . . .
met-terlo in bur - let-ta!
fool him and we'll chide him.
Oh! oh! che spasso!
. . . and hit and haunt him!
Che ven -
. . . and de -
Che alle - gri-a!
We will cool him . . .
pp

UN POCO MENO ♩. = 100
(turning from one to the other, all huddling together)
A
Quell'o_tre! quel ti_ - - - - - no!
This mon-strous de-cant - - - - - er,
N
M
_det_ta!
-ride him!
Un flutto in tem_
Come up from the
(to Alice)
Q
Quell'uom è un can - no - ne,
That gun with its thun - der,
UN POCO MENO ♩. = 100
(24)
Quel Re del_le pan - - - -
This prince of di - la - - - -
(to Alice)
Se ordi_sci u_na bur_la
Oh, let me, dear Moth-er,
_pe_sta Git_tò sul_la re_na
o-cean To har-ry and hound us,
Se scoppia ci
We'll damp-en its
ben staccato

A
- - çie,
- - - tion,
Ci ha anco_ra le
Shall har-vest vex-
N
Vo'anch'io la mia
Share frol - ic and
par_te. Se or_disci una
laugh-ter. This game like no
M
Di Windsor co _ de_sta Vo_ra_ce ba _ le_na, Co _ de_sta vo _
A mon-ster has bound us In fear and com - mo-tion. A mon-ster has
Q
spac _ cia,
pow - der,
mf
A
cian_ce Del bel vagheg_gi no.
- a - tion From frol - ic and ban-ter!
Quel _ l'o_tre! quel
This mon-strous de -
N
bur_la Vo'anch'io la mia par_te,
oth - er Will ring down the raft-er.
Vo'anch'i _ o,
Please let me,
M
_ra _ ce, Vo_ra_ce ba _ le_na.
bound us In fear and com - mo-tion.
Di Windsor
A mon-ster
Q
Se scoppia ci spaccia, Se
And laugh e-ven loud-er While

A
ti_no! Quel_l'o_tre! Quel ti_no!
-cant-er, This mon-strous de-cant-er.
N
vo'anch'i_o, anch'io la mia parte.
dear Moth-er, Share frol-ic and laugh-ter.
M
co_de_sta Vo_ra_ce ba_le_na.
has bound us In fear and com-mo-tion.
Q
scoppia, se scoppia ci spaccia.
call-ing, yes, call-ing its blun-der!
mf
PIÙ MODERATO ♩. = 88
sottovoce
Quel_l'o_tre! quel ti_no! Quel Re del_le pancie, Ci ha anco_ra le
This mon-strous de-cant-er, This prince of di-la-tion, Shall har-vest vex-
sottovoce
Se or di_sci u_na bur_la Vo'anch'io la mia par_te. Con_vie_ne con
Oh, let me, dear Moth-er, Share frol-ic and laugh-ter. This game like no
sottovoce
Quell'uom è un can_no_ne, Se scoppia ci spaccia. Co_lui, se l'ab_
Come up from the o-cean To har-ry and hound us, A mon-ster has
sottovoce
Un flutto in tem_pe_sta Git_tò sul_la re_na Di Windsor co_
This gun with its thun-der, We'll damp-en its pow-der And laugh e-ven
PIÙ MODERATO ♩. = 88
(25) ppp
(ad libitum, se necessario)
ppp

A
ciance Del bel vagheggi_no. E l'o_lio gli sgocciola Dal_l'a_di_pe un
- a-tion From frol-ic and ban-ter! His crass no-to-ri-e-ty Will be his per-
N
_dur_la Con sen_no, con ar_te. L'agguato ov'ei sdrucciola Convien ch'ei non
oth-er Will ring down the raft-er. De-ny-ing our am-i-ty We'll gai-ly for-
M
_braccia, Ti schiaccia Giu_no_ne. Ma cer_to si spap_po_la Quel mostro a un tuo
bound us In fear and com-mo-tion. So let's be u-nan-i-mous And plan our de-
Q
_de_sta Vo_ra_ce ba_le_na. Ma qui non ha spa_zio Da far_si più
loud-er While call-ing its blun-der! But as you pur-sue him And shrewd-ly en-
A
_tic_cio E ancora ei ne snocciola La strofa e il bis_tic_cio! Lasciam ch'ei le
- di-tion, We'll teach him so-bri-e-ty But cause no sus-pi-cion. He'll fol-low us
N
scerna. Già prese una luccio_la Per u_na lan_ter_na. Che il gio_co ri_
- sake him, And black-est ca-lam-i-ty Will soon o-ver-take him. His sil-ly pre-
M
cenno E corre alla trappo_la E perde il suo senno. Po_ten_za d'un
- fenc-es! This man pu-sil-lan-i-mous Let's bring to his sens-es! Our ways must be
Q
pingue Ne fe_cer già stra_zio Le vo_stre tre lin_gue. Tre lin_gue più al_
- snare him, Be-fore you un-do him You bet-ter be-ware him: He's art-ful and

A
N
M
Q
pronte Sue ciarle ne spif-fe-ri, Fa-rà come i pif-fe-ri Che sceser dal
glad-ly And tum-ble more read-i-ly, For he who courts head-i-ly, Will of-ten court
-e-sca Perciò più non du-bi-to Per co-glierlo su-bi-to Bi-sogna offrir
-ten-sions, His shak-y mo-ral-i-ty, In-crease his mor-tal-i-ty, To dread-ful di-
fra-gil Sor-ri-so di don-na! Scï-en-za d'un a-gi-le Movenza di
cun-ning, Dis-creet and be-liev-a-ble. Our end is a-chiev-a-ble. Hi-lar-ious and
-le-gre D'un trillo di nacchere, Che spargon più chiacchiere Di sei cin-gal-
wil-y, Of can-ny fe-lin-i-ty, And may trick your trin-i-ty Un-less you act
p
mon-te. Ve-drai che se ab-bin-do-lo Quel gros-so com-
bad-ly. Watch out, you po-lyg-a-mist Dis-guised as a
l'e-sca. E se i sci-lin-gua-gno-li Sa-pre-mo a-do-
-men-sion. You sym-bol of van-i-ty, You lech-er, you
gon-na! Se il vi-schio l'im-pe-go-la Lo u-dre-mo stril-
stun-ning. Your shame-less du-plic-i-ty, You scoun-drel, you
-le-gre. Tal sem-pre s'e-sì-la-ri Quel bel cin-guet-
sly-ly! For all his fat-u-i-ty He's quick as a

(From the right, enter Ford, followed by Dr. Cajus; then Bardolph, Pistol and Fenton.)
pp
A
-par Più le-sto d'un guin-do-lo, Più le-sto d'un
-vat: The fate of a big-a-mist, A tri-or tet-
N
-prar, Ve-dre-mo a ri-ga-gno-li, Ve-dre-mo a ri-
gnat, We'll bring you to san-i-ty, Re-spect and ur-
M
-lar. E al-lor la sua fre-go-la, E al-lor la sua
rat, Will bring us fe-lic-i-ty And bring you pub-
Q
-tar. Co-sì so-glion l'i-la-ri, Co-sì so-glion
cat. 'T will take in-gen-u-i-ty And great as-sid-
A
guin-do-lo, più le-sto, più le-sto, Lo fac-cio gi-
-rag-a-mist Is some-thing to fear, A-bove all when you're
N
-ga-gno-li, ve-dre-mo, ve-dre-mo, Quel-l'or-co su-
-ban-i-ty, Yes, all these you'll learn As we hand you your
M
fre-go-la, Ve-dre-mo, ve-dre-mo, ve-dre-mo svam-
-lic-i-ty... You'll nev-er a-gain Want to bar-gain for
Q
l'i-la-ri, Co-sì so-glion l'i-la-ri Co-ma-ri ciar-
-u-i-ty To punc-ture his pride And to bat-ter him

♩. = 88
LO STESSO TEMPO *(The women leave together to the left; every once in a while one or the other is seen through the bushes to the rear, unnoticed by the men.)*

A
-rar.
fat!

N
-dar.
hat!

M
-par.
that!

Q
-lar.
flat.

(all speaking to Mr. Ford, softly but in great agitation)

Dr. CAJUS *(to Ford)* *sottovoce*
È un ri-baldo, un furbo, un la-dro, Un fur-fan-te, un turco, un
He's a li-ar and a lech-er, All he knows is rape and

BARDOLFO *(to Ford)* *sottovoce*
Falstaff, sì, ri-pe-to,
Fal-staff, as I keep re-

𝅗𝅥 = 88
LO STESSO MOVIMENTO

(26)
pp

FENTON *(to Ford)* *sottovoce*
Se vo-le-te io non mi pe-ri-to Di ri-durlo al-la ra-
For his scan-dal-ous te-mer-i-ty I should like to see him

Dr. C
vandalo; L'altro dì mandò a soq-qua-dro La mia casa e fu u-no
rob-ber-y. He's a lout and rake and retch-er And a pa-ra-gon of

B
giu-ro, sì, ri-pe-to, giu-ro, giu-ro, (Per mia bocca il ciel v'il-
-peat-ing, Is a gen-i-us at cheat-ing. Mas-ter Ford, let me re-

PISTOLA *(to Ford)* *sottovoce*
Sir John Falstaff già v'ap-
Mas-ter Ford, oh let me

ALI.
Quel - l'o - tre! Quel ti - no!
This mon - ster, this mon - ster,
NAN.
Quel - l'o - tre! Quel
This bar - rel, this
MEG
Quel - l'o - tre! Quel ti - no!
This mon - ster, this mon - ster,
QUIC.
Quel - l'o - tre! Quel
This bar - rel, this
FEN
- gio - ne Col - le brusche o col - le buo - ne, Col - le brusche o col - le
suf - fer. I will beat the bra - zen bluff - er, Turn - ing rough and ev - er
Dr. C
scanda - lo. Se un pro - cesso og - gi gl'in - ta - volo Sconte - rà le sue ra -
snob - ber - y. He has brok - en all my crock - er - y, rode my mare un - til she's
B
- lu - mina) Con - tro voi, John Falstaff
- it - er - ate: (to himself, then to the others) It is you he will ob -
FORD
Un ron - zio di vespe e d'avi - di Ca - la - bron bronto - la -
Ah, a - round me all this flummer - y Has be - gun to o - ver -
P
- pre - sta, Sir John Falstaff già v'ap - pre - sta, Messer Ford, un gran pe -
warn you, Ev - ry man in town will scorn you. Fal - staff has a plan per -

A
Quel - l'o - - - - - - -
this mon - - - - - - -
N
ti - no! Quel - l'o - - - - - - -
bar - rel, this mon - - - - - - -
M
Quel - l'o - - - - - - -
this mon - - - - - - -
Q
ti - no! Quel - l'o - - - - - - -
bar, - rel, this mon - - - - - - -
FEN
buo - ne, E pa-garlo al par del me - ri - to, Pa - garlo al par del
rough - er, And my fu - ry and se - ver - i - ty Will low - er his pros -
Dr. C
- pi - ne. Ma la sua più de-gna fi - ne Sia d'an - dare in man del
dy - ing. Dev-il take him, keep him fry - ing As re - ward for all his
B
rumi-na Un progetto alquanto im-
- lit - er - ate. If you're deaf to my en- -
FOR
- men - to, Un rombar di nem-bi gravi-di D'u-ra - gani è quel ch'io
- come - me Like a bum-bling kind of mum-mer-y Which will stun me and be -
P
-ri-co-lo. Già vi pen-de sul-la te - sta Qualche co-sa a perpen-
-fid- i - ous, For he wish-es to a - dorn you With a head gear worse than
pp

A
_tre!
- ster!
N
_tre!
- ster!
M
_tre!
- ster!
Q
_tre!
- ster!
FEN
me_ri_to. Mi dà co_re e mi sol _ le_ti_ca,
-per- i -ty. I can feel my sens-es quiv-er-ing,
D.r C
diavo_lo. È un ri _ bal_do,
mock-er-y. He's a scoun-drel,
B
-pu _ ro. Son uom d'arme e quell'in _ fa _ me Più non vo' che v'impoz_
-treat - ing. I'm a sol-dier but no boo - ty Ev-er dulls my sen-si -
FOR
sen_to.
-numb me.
P
_di_co_lo. Mes_ser
hid-e-ous. I know
p stacc.

A
N
M
Q
EN
(E sarà u_na giostra ga - ia, ga_ia, ga - - -
And my heart flies high, my heart flies ev-er high- - -
C
è un ri_baldo, un turco, un
He's a lout and rake and
B
_zangheri. Non vor - rei, no, escir dai gangheri Del_l'o_nor per un re_
- tiv - i - ty And com - pels me to ac - tiv - i - ty Which of-fends my sense of
OR
P
Ford, fui già un Ar - mige_ro
well I was un - sa-vor-y.
di quell'uom dall'am_pia
Fal-staff made me lose my

(from a distance)
A
Quel - l'o - - -
This mon- - -
N
Quel - l'o - - -
This mon- - -
(from a distance)
M
Quel - l'o - - -
This mon- - -
Q
Quel - l'o - - -
This mon- - -
FEN
- - ia,)
- - er,
Di sfondar quel - la ven -
When I think of that old
Dr.C.
la - dro, Se un pro - cesso og - gi gl'in - tavolo Sconte - rà le sue ra -
lech-er, who has brok-en all my crock-er-y, rode my mare un - til she's
B
- a - me. Mes - ser Ford, l'uom av - vi - sa - to Non è sal - vo che a me -
du - ty. Mas-ter Ford, I know you need me: Let my warn-ing come in
FOR
Il cerèbro un ebro al - lucina Turba - men - to di pa -
How I wish they would be sen-si-ble So I'd know what each is
P
cu - te,
sens - es.
Or mi pento e mi mo -
I re - pent and hope my

A
N
M
Q
FEN
DrC
B
FOR
P
_tre! Quel ti
_ster, this bar-
_tre! Quel ti
_ster, this bar-
_tre! Quel ti
_ster, this bar-
_tre! Quel ti
_ster, this bar-
_tra_ia Iperbo_li _co a _po
li-ar On his knees, all spent and
_pi_ne. Ma la sua più degna fi _ ne Sia d'an_dare in man del
dy-ing. Dev-il take him, keep him fry-ing As re-ward for all his
_tà. Tocca a voi d'ordir l'ag_gua_to Che l'ag_gua_to stor _ ne
time: It is you who now must heed me To pre-vent this ug - ly
_u_ra Ciò che intorno a me si buccina È un su_sur_ro di con
do-ing! Though they are in-com-pre-hen-si-ble I can feel a dan - ger
_rigero. Per ra_gio_ni di sa
brav-er-y Will a-tone for my of-

(The women disappear completely.)
A
- - no!
- - rel!-
N
- - no!
- - rel!
M
- - no!
- - rel!
Q
- - no!
- - rel!
FEN
-plettica. Col consi-glio o col-la spa-da Se lo trovo al tu per
shiv-er-ing. I will first ap-peal to rea-son, But if this should not do
Dr. C
diavolo. E quei du-e che a-vete ac-
mock-er-y. These two ras-cals right here be-
B
-rà. Tocca a voi d'ordir l'ag-
crime! Mas-ter Ford, I know you
FOR
-giu-ra. Parlan quattro ed u-no a-scol-ta, Qual dei quattro ascolte-
brew-ing. I should high-ly praise and cheer you If you on-ly were a
P
-lu-te. La minaccia or v'è sco-per-ta, Or v'è no-to il ciurma-
-fenc-es. There is noth-ing more to men-tion, Now the rest is up to

TEN
tu, Se lo tro_vo al tu per
well, Yes, if this should not do
D.r C
_can_to Gen_ti son di sua tri_
_side you: They are e - vil through and
B
_gua_to, Che l'ag_gua_to stor_ne_
need me: Let my warn-ing come in
FOR
_rò? Qual dei quattro a_scol_te_
_ware: Who speaks first I do not
P
_dor. Sta_te all'er_ta, all'er_ta, al_l'er - - - - - - -
you: Be on guard and pay at_ten - - - - - - -
FOR
tu, O lui va per la sua strada, O l'as_segno a Belze_
well, then it would amount to treason Not to send him down to
_bù, Non son due stinchi di santo Nè son fio_ri di vir_
through. Let my friendly council guide you: I'd be-ware if I were
_rà, Tocca a voi d'or_dir l'agguato Che l'aggua_to storne_
time: It is you who now must heed me To pre-vent this ug-ly
_rò? Se par_laste uno alla volta, se parlaste uno alla volta Forse allor v'in_tende_
care: Four to speak and one to hear you Four to speak and one to hear you This indeed is hardly
_ta! State all'erta, all'erta, al_l'erta! Qui si trat_ta dell'o_
_tion, Be on guard and pay at - ten-tion And find out what he will
pp
pppp
f
(27)

poco cres.
FEN
-bù, Se lo tro-vo al tu per tu, O lui va per la sua
Hell! If he should be deaf to rea-son Then it would a-mount to
D.r C
-tù, Non son due stin-chi di san-to, Non son due stin-chi di
you! These two ras-cals here be-side you: Let my friend-ly coun-cil
B
rà, Toc-ca a voi d'or-dir l'ag-gua-to, Toc-ca a voi d'or-dir l'ag-
crime! Mas-ter Ford, I know you need me: It is you who now must
FOR
-rò, Se par-la-ste uno al-la vol-ta, Se par-la-ste uno al-la
fair! You should know that I am near you. Four to speak and one to
P
-nor, Or v'è no-to il ciur-ma-dor. Sta-te al-l'er-ta, al-l'er-ta, al-
do! There is noth-ing more to mention Be on guard and pay at-
p poco cres.
strada, O l'as-segno a Belze-bù.
trea-son Not to send him down to Hell!
Sempre lo stesso tempo
santo Nè son fio-ri di vir-tù.
guide you. They are e-vil through and through!
-guato Che l'agguato storne-rà.
heed me. To pre-vent this ug-ly crime!
(to Pistol)
volta Forse allor v'in-tende-rò.
hear you. This in-deed is hard-ly fair!
Ripe-ti.
Con-tin-ue!
(to Ford)
-l'erta Qui si trat-ta dell'o-nor.
-ten-tion And find out what he will do!
Sempre lo stesso tempo
(28)
In due pa-
I'll tell you
ff

_ro _ le:
short-ly:
L'e _ nor _ me Fal _ staff
Sir Fal - staff round and
pp leggiero
vuo _ le
port - ly
En _ trar nel vo _ stro
Is yearn - ing for some
tet _ to, Bec_car_vi la con _ sor_te, Sfon_dar la cas_sa
head - room. Your till could be his treas-ure, Your wife pro-vide his
p
f
forte E...
pleas-ure While . . .
e.......... sconquassar_vi il
while___ he com-mands your
ff
ff
p

D^r C.
Ca _ spita!
Dash it all!
FOR.
Quan - - ti guai!
Ah, I'll die!
P
let _ to.
bed - room!
ff
BAR.
(to Ford)
Già le scrisse un bi _ gliet _ to...
And a let - ter he penned her. . .
P
(interrupting him)
Ma
. . . through
p

quel messag _ gio ab _ biet _ _ to ri _ cu _
me he meant to send her. 'No!' said
BAR.
Ri _ cu _ sai.
So did I.
_ sai.
I.
p
Ba _ da _ _ _
Re - mem _ _ _
Bada _ te a voi!
So be on guard!

B
P
- te!
- ber: . . .
Fal - staff le occhieggia tut - te Che sie - no bel - le o
For him no wom - an's ho - ly, Tall, lean, or ro - ly -
sf
p
B
P
Tutte! tutte! tutte!
Single, maiden, matron!
brutte Pul - zelle o mari - tate. Tutte! tutte!
- po - ly, In May or in De - cem - ber! Married, matron!
sf
p
f
p
B
pp
La coro - na che adorna D'Atteòn l'ir - te chiome Su voi già
Or the crown - ing a - dorn - ment of Ac - tae - on's fair brow Will be found on

sottovoce
B
spun_ta.
you, Sir.
Le car - - -
The horns,
FORD
Come sareb_be a dir?
What-do-you mean by that?
Brutta pa_
Ghast-ly ex-
(29)
Dr. C.
Ha voglie vo_ra _ ci il Ca_va _ lier.
The gen-tle-man's greed shocks me. in - deed!
B
_na.
Sir!
FOR
_ ro_la!
- pres-sion!
Sor_ve_glie_rò la
My wife and that old
mf
(The four women re-enter from the left.)
FOR
moglie. Sor_ve_glie_rò il mes _ se _ re. Sal_var vo'i be-_ni
charm-er, That knight in rust-ing arm - or: She still be longs to
f
mf

ALI.
(seeing Ford)
(È
'Tis
NAN.
(seeing Fenton)
(È Lui.)
'Tis he!
FEN.
(seeing Ann)
(È Lei.)
'Tis she!
(seeing Alice)
FOR
miei Dagl'appe_titi al_trui.
me, This much I guar-an - tee!
(È Lei.)
'Tis she!
f
pp
(to the others, referring to Ford)
sottovoce
3
A
Lui.)
he!
(S'egli sa_pesse!...
If he should guess it ! . .
N
Gua_i!
My!
MEG. (to Alice, pointing to Ford)
(È Lui.)
'Tis he!
Dr. C. (to Ford, pointing to Alice)
(È Lei.)
'Tis she!

(Ford, Dr. Cajus, Bardolph and Pistol leave to the right. Fenton stays on stage.)
Schiviamo i passi suo_i.
We'd bet-ter now a - void him.
Assa _ i!
In-sane - ly.
Ford è ge _ lo _ so?
Why? Is he jeal-ous?
(Alice, Meg and Quickly leave to the left. Ann stays on stage.)
Badiamo a noi.)
We'd bet-ter hide!
QUIC.
Zitto!
Si-lence!
(putting her forefinger to her lips to caution him)
senza tempo
Ssssss. Taci. Che vuoi? In fretta.
Qui-et! 'Tis you? But quick-ly!
(from the bushes, softly calling Ann)
senza tempo
Pst, pst. Nan_netta. Vien qua. Due baci. In
Pst! Ann! My dar-ling, come here! Come, kiss me! Yes,
ppp
col canto

ALLEGRETTO ♩=126
(rapid exchange of kisses)
FEN
fretta.
quick-ly!
(30)
ALLEGRETTO ♩=126
p
p
NAN.
dolciss.
Lab_bra di fo _ co!
Lips, oh so burn - ing!
Che il va_go
Lips where my
FEN
dolciss.
Lab_bra di fio - re!..
Lips red as ros - es!
dolciss.
pp con espress.
N
gio _ co San_no d'a _ mo _ re.
yearn - ing sweet-ly re - pos - es!
FEN
Che spargon ciar _ le,
Some-times re - veal - ing

Che mo-stran per - le, Bel-le a ve - der - le, Dol - - ci a ba -
pearls shin-ing bright - ly, Kiss-ing me light - ly, wound - - ing or
(tries to embrace her)
ciar - le! Lab - bra leg - gia - - dre!
heal - ing! Kiss - es that haunt me...
NAN.
(defending herself and looking around)
Man malan - dri - ne!
Bra - zen of - fend - er!
Ci - glia assas -
Glanc - es so

string.
N
Impru_
They will
(tries to kiss her again)
FEN
_si _ ne! Pu_pil _ le ladre!
ten _ der, Why do you taunt me?
T'a_mo!...
Kiss me!
p
string.
_den_te. No..........
hear us! No!
(freeing herself)
Basta.
Ras-cal!
Sì, due ba_ci.
Please . . . two kiss - es!
Mi pia_ci
Ah, how I
(They leave each other while the
women re-enter.)
Vien gente.
They're near us.
tanto!
love you!
(31)
f
p
mf
rall..........

PIÙ LENTO ♩=80
(continuing Fenton's song)
Anzi rin_
"Trust in the
(hiding behind the bushes)
Bocca ba _ cia _ ta non per_de ven_tu _ ra...
"Just kiss me soon, — and you al-ways will do it!"
PIÙ LENTO ♩=80
pp
_no _ va come fa la lu
moon, — love-will-al-ways-re - new
ppp
na, co _ me fa la
it, al-ways will re-
dim.
morendo e allarg.
lu na.
- new it!"
morendo e allarg. a tempo

(Re-enter Alice, Meg, Mrs. Quickly. Ann to the rear.)
ALLEGRO 𝅗𝅥 = 126
animando un poco
(32)
p
cres.
mf
cres.
f
ff
ALICE (to the others)
Fal - staff m'ha can-zo - na-ta.
Fal - staff tells us a fa-ble.
MEG.
Me - ri-ta un gran ca-
Wait — till we turn the
M
-sti-go.
ta - ble!
(33)
f

Se gli scri_ves _ si un ri _ _ go?...
What if I wrote a let - - ter?
NAN.
(rejoining the others unobtrusively)
Val meglio un'am_ba_
A mes-sen - ger were
pp
Sì.
Yes.
QUIC. _sciata.
bet-ter.
Sì.
Yes.
Sì.
Yes.
Sì.
Yes.
a tempo
POCO PIÙ LENTO ♩=88

ALI.
(to Quickly)
Da quel bri_gan_te tu an_drai...
The one to see him is you,
A
(thinking it over)
Lo a_de_schi al_l'of _ fa d'un ri_trovo ga_lan_te con
And you in - vite him to a ten-der ap-point-ment with
p
A
string.
COME PRIMA
con brio
me.
me.
Pri _ ma, per at_ti_rar_lo a
First we will bait a trap to
NAN.
Che bel_la bur_la!
It will de - light him.
QUIC.
Quest'è gagliof_fa!
That will ex-cite him.
COME PRIMA
string.
p

noi lo lu_singhia - mo, e poi glie_le cantiamo in
lure him and se-cure him. And then . . . and then we'll let him
e poi...
And then?
ri_ma.
have it!
QUIC.
È un
The
Non me_ri_ta ri - guardo.
A long be-lat-ed mat-ter!
mf
bo - ve.
bull - dog!
MEG.
È un mon - te di
The moun - tain of
È un uo_mo sen_za fe_de.
This mis-cre-ant se-duc-er!

A
lar_do.
bat - ter!
È un ghiotton che scia_
He is eat - ing and
M
Non me_ri_ta cle_menza.
We'll show him no com - pas-sion.
cres.
A
_lac_qua tutto il suo aver nel cuo_co.
NAN.
drink - ing un-til his sens - es fail him.
Lo tuf_fe_rem nel_
We'll dunk him till he's
cres. sempre
A
Lo ar_ro_sti_re_mo al fuo_co.
. . . and boil and roast and scale him!
Che alle_
This is
N
_l'acqua.
sink - ing . . .
Che gio_ia!
De - light-ful!
cres.

f
gri_a!
price-less!
Che gioia, che gioia, che gioia, che
En-chant-ing, en-chant-ing, en-chant-ing, en -
Che gioia, che gioia, che gioia, che
En-chant-ing, en-chant-ing, en-chant-ing, en -
MEG.
Che gio - ia! che gioia, che gioia, che gioia, che gioia, che
En-chant - ing, en-chant-ing, en-chant-ing, en-chant-ing, en-chant-ing, en -
QUIC.
Che gio - ia! che gioia, che gioia, che gioia, che gioia, che
En-chant - ing, en-chant-ing, en-chant-ing, en-chant-ing, en-chant-ing, en -
cres.
gio - - - - ia!
-chant - - - - ing!
gio - - - - ia!
-chant - - - - ing!
(to Quickly)
gio - - - - ia! Pro -
-chant - - - - ing! You
gio - - - - ia!
-chant - - - - ing!
(34)
dim.

M
Q
- cac_cia di far be_ne la tua par_te.
know your part, now play it to per - fec-tion!
(noticing Fenton hiding nearby)
Chi
Who
p
(The women, except Ann, rapidly exit to the right. Fenton comes forward as soon as they are gone.)
ALL.tto COME PRIMA ♩ = 126
Là c'è qual_cun che spi_a.
Be-ware! There's some-one spy-ing!
vie - ne?
is this?
ALL.tto COME PRIMA ♩ = 126
p
p

NAN.
(pretending to defy him)
Torno alla ga_ra. Fe_ri _sci!
You won't em-brace me. Just try it!
(approaching Ann)
FEN.
Torno all'as_sal_to.
Now I shall storm you.
dolciss.
pp con espress.
(He tries to kiss her. She covers her face with her hand which Fenton kisses. Then she raises her hand too high for him to reach it with his lips.)
La mi_ra è in al_to.
I shall re - form you.
Pa_ra!
Face me!
L'a_mor è un a_gi_le tor_ne_o, sua cor_te
In love the frail_and fair de-fend-er Will in the

N
vuol che il più fragi_le vin_ _ca il più for_te.
end be vic - to-rious And will win sur - ren - der.
FEN.
M'ar_mo,.. ti guar_do. T'a_spetto al
Soon I shall bind you And shall dis -
leggeriss.
N
Il labbro è l'ar _ co.
But I will charm you.
FEN
var_co. E il ba_cio è il
-arm you. My kiss will
3
3
3

dardo. Bada!... la freccia fa_tal già scocca dal_la mia
(35)
find you. Care-ful! Your tress-es So soft and ten-der Will now sur-
ppp legato
poco cres.
NAN.
(puts one of her tresses around his neck, as if to capture him)
(He kisses her hair.)
Ec_co_ti av_vinto.
Caught is the sin-ner!
boc_ca sulla tua treccia.
-ren-der To my ca-ress-es.
p
ppp
Io son fe_ri_ta
Wound-ed and bleed-ing,
Chie_do la vi_ta!
Ah, heed my plead-ing!
ppp

N
FEN
ma tu sei vinto.
I am the win-ner.
Pie_tà! pie_tà! Fac_
I yield the field, hand
p
E poi?
. . . and then?
con grazia
_cia_mo la pace e poi...
o-ver my weap-on, and then . .
Se vuoi, ricomin_
And then we start it all
Bello è quel gio _ co che du_ra
Let me in-vite you! I love to
_ciamo.
o-ver.
pp e stacc.

po - co.
fight you . . .
Basta.
lat-er!
A-mor mi - o!
Do not flee me!
(exits to the right)
Vien gen-te..
I hear them . . .
Ad - di - o!
they'll see me!
(36) mf
FEN.
(withdrawing)
PIÙ LENTO
♩=80
PIÙ LENTO
Bocca ba - cia - ta non perde ven -
"Just kiss me soon, and you al-ways will
rall.
pp
NAN.
(answering him from offstage)
dolciss.
An-zi rin - no - va co-me fa la lu -
"Trust in the moon, love will al-ways re - new
- tu - ra.
do it!"

N
na, come
it, al-ways
FEN
Bocca ba - cia - ta non per - de ven - tu - ra,
Oh, kiss me soon, and you al - ways will do it,
dolce
ppp
allarg. e morendo
fa la lu
will re - new
non per - de ven - tu
you al - ways will do
ALL°. VIVO ♩= 126
(Re-enter Ford, Dr. Cajus, Bardolph, and Pistol. Fenton rejoins them presently.)
na.
it!"
ra.
it!"
(37)
f

(to Ford)
U_drai quanta egli sfog_gia magni_loquenza al-
To lis - ten to his bray - ing makes an-y man a
p
_te - ra.
FORD mar - tyr.
Di - ceste ch'egli alloggia... Dove?
You mentioned where he's staying . . . tell me!
Al_la Giarret_
Right there at the
p
A lui m'annun_cie - re - te,
You ask him to re - ceive me,
_tie _ ra,
"Gar - ter"
cantando
p
(p)
mf

FOR
Ma— con un fal - so no - - me,
Hid - ing my name and sta - tion!
(3)
(p)
(3)
mf
FOR
Po_scia ve_dre - - te co - me Lo pi_glio nel_la
John Fal-staff's cas - - ti - ga - tion Is un - der - way, be -
BAR.
In ciarle non m'in_golfo.
Re-gard me as your serv-ant!
FOR
re_te. Ma... non u_na pa_ro_la.
- lieve me! If you're dis-creet and loy - al . . .
f
f
ff

senza misura
Io mi chiamo Bardol - fo.
I am Bar-dolph, the fer-vent.
Siam d'accor - do.
Will you prom-ise?
Io mi chiamo Pi - sto - la.
I am Pis tol, the trust-y.
col canto
L'arcano custodirem.
Our word is as good as gold . . .
Sì.
Yes.
Siam d'accordo tutti.
Are we in a-gree-ment?
Qua la
On your
Son sordo e muto.
. . . and e - ven bet-ter.
Sì.
Yes.

(The four women appear in the background.)
Dr. C. ALL°. COME PRIMA 𝅗𝅥 = 88
(to Ford) pp
Del tuo bar_ba_ro dia-
E-ven when of ut-most
B
(to Ford) pp
Mes_ser Ford, un in-for-
Mas-ter Ford, you must be
FOR
mano.
hon-or?
P
(to Ford) pp
Voi do_ve-te empir_gli il
One good way to make him
ALL°. COME PRIMA 𝅗𝅥 = 88
(38) pp
pp stacc.
Dr. C
-gnosti_co For_se il male è assai men bar_ba_ro. Ti convien ten_tar la
grav-i-ty A dis-ease is of-ten cur-a-ble. Na-ture's pow-er will sur-
B
-tu-nio Ma_ri_tal in voi s'in-cor_po_ra. Se non sie_te astu_to e
dras-tic For this case is most pre-car-i-ous: With your wife a to-tal
P
ca_li_ce Trat_to, trat_to in_ter_ro-gando_lo Per ten_tar se vi ri-
pli-a-ble Is to flat-ter his cu-pid-i-ty. You re-mem-ber what I

ALI.
Tutte insieme
Quel_l'o_tre! Quel
This mon-strous de-
NAN.
Se or-di-sci u-na
Oh, let me, dear
MEG
Tutte insieme
Ve-drai che a un tuo
Let's plan our de-
QUIC.
Tre lin-gue più al-
He's art-ful and
C
pro-va Mo-le-stis-si-ma del ver, Ti convien ten-tar la
-prise you And as-sist you when you're ill. Na-ture's pow-er will sur-
B
cau-to Quel sir John vi tra-di-rà, Se non sie-te a-stu-to e
stran-ger Who will sure-ly go too far, With your wife a to-tal
P
-e-sca Di tro-var del no-do il bando-lo, Per ten-tar se vi ri-
told you Of his lik-ing for liq-uid-i-ty. You re-mem-ber what I

A
ti - no! Quel Re del - le pan - cie Ci ha anco - ra le
- cant - er This prince of di - la - tion, Shall har - vest vex -
N
bur - la Vo' anch'io la mia par - te Con - vie - ne con -
Moth - er, Share frol - ic and laugh - ter. This game like no
M
cen - no Quel mo - stro si spap - po - la E per - de il suo
- fenc - es! So let's be u - nan - i - mous. Let's bring to his
Q
- le - gre D'un tril - lo di nac - che - re, Che spar - gon più
wil - y, Of can - ny fe - lin - i - ty, And may trick your
FEN.
(to himself)
Qua bar - bot - ta un crocchio d'uomi - ni,
Ah, these men and all this blab - ber - ing,
D.r C
pro - va Mo - le - stis - si - ma del
- prise you And as - sist you when you're
B
cau - to Quel sir John vi tra - di -
stran - ger Who will sure - ly go too
P
- e - sca Di tro - var del no - do il
told you Of his lik - ing for liq -

cian - ce Del bel va - gheg - gi - no! Quel-
- a - tion, From frol - ic and ban - ter! The
- dur - la Con sen - no e con ar - te. Quel-
oth - er, Will ring down the raft - er. The
sen - no E cor - re al - la trappola. Quel
sens es, This man pu - sil - lan - i-mous. The
chiacchiere Di sei cin - gal - le - gre. Quel-
trin - i - ty Un - less you act sly - ly. The
C'è nel - l'a - ria una ma - lì - a
They are plan-ning and are schem-ing,
ver. Così avvien col sapor
ill. In a mat - ter of de -
- rà. Quel paf - fu - to ple - ni -
far! Yes, I know it seems fan -
(to Bardolph)
Tu ve - drai se bene a -
You will see my vir - tu -
bando - lo. Come all'acqua inclina il
- uid - i - ty. For it is quite un - de -

A
N
M
Q
FEN
Dr. C
B
FOR
P
-l'o - - - - - - - - - tre! Quel
mon - - - - - - - - - ster, the
-l'o - - - - - - - - - tre! Quel
mon - - - - - - - - - ster, the
mo - - - - - - - - - stro! Quel
mon - - - - - - - - - ster, the
-l'o - - - - - - - - - tre! Quel
mon - - - - - - - - - ster, the
C'è nel - l'a - - - ria
They are plan - - - ning
o-sti-co Del gi-ne-pro o del ra-barba-ro; Il benes-se-re rin-
-prav-i-ty That to you seems un-en-dur-a-ble, As a doc-tor I ad-
-lu-nio Che il co-lor del vi-no im-porpo-ra Trovereb-be un pa-sto
-tas-tic, But that drunk-ard is ne-far-i-ous. You will run a fa-tal
-dope-ra L'ar-te mia con quel-l'in-fa-me; E sarà prez-zo del-
-os-i-ty In the way I shall en-snare him, Then the ti-ger-ish fe-
sa-li-ce Co-sì al vin quel Ca-va-lier. Scove-re-te la sua
-ni-a-ble, Wine will quick-ly make him fall. In his arms he will en-

ti - - - - - - - - no! Ve_drai che se ab_
bar- - - - - - - - rel! Watch out, you po -
ti - - - - - - - - no! E se i sci _ lin -
bar- - - - - - - - rel! You sym - bol of
mo - - - - - - - - stro! Se il vi _ schio lo im_
bar- - - - - - - - rel! Your shame-less du -
ti - - - - - - - - no! Tal sem_pre s'e -
bar- - - - - - - - rel! For all his fat -
u _ na ma _ lì - - - a
and they are schem- - - ing.
_ no _ va L'a_ma_ris _ si _ mo bic _ chier.
- vise you: Hold your nose and take a pill!
lau _ to Nel _ la vostra in_ge_nui _ tà.
dan - ger Leav-ing mat- ters as they are.
_l'o_pe_ra S'io di_sco_pro le sue tra _ me.
- roc- i - ty I'll dis- play when I shall tear him.
tre _ sca Sco_pri _ re_te il suo pen _ sier.
-fold you And at last will tell you all.

A
_bin_do_lo Quel gros _ so com _ par...... Più le _ sto d'un
_lyg-a-mist Dis-guised as a vat,___ The fate of a
N
_guagnoli Sa_pre_mo a_do _ prar..... Ve_dre_mo a ri _
van-i-ty, You lech-er, you gnat,___ We'll bring you to
M
_pe_go_la Lo u_dre_mo stril _ lar....... E al_lor la sua
-plic-i-ty, You scoun-drel, you rat,___ Will bring you pub-
Q
_si_la_ri Quel bel cin_guet _ tar,...... Co _ sì so_glion
-u-i-ty He's quick as a cat:___ 'Twill take in-gen-
FEN
Là cin_guetta un stuol di fe_mi_ne,
O-ver there the wom-en jab-ber-ing...
Dr. C
B
FOR
P

A
guindolo Lo fac_cio gi - rar.
big-a-mist Is sad when you're fat!
N
-gagnoli Quel - l'or - co su - dar.
san-i-ty, And hand you your hat.
M
frego_la Ve - dre - mo svam - par.
-lic-i-ty, We'll wa-ger on that!
Q
l'i_la_ri Co - ma - ri ciar - lar.
-u-i-ty To bat-ter him flat.
EN
Spira un vento agi_ta - tor.
How did all this clam-or start?
C
Ma quei due che a_ve_te ac_
The two ras-cals here be -
B
Messer Ford, l'uom av_vi -
Mas-ter Ford, I know you
OR
Tu ve_drai se be_ne a_
You will see my vir-tu -
P
p staccato
pp

A
p
Più le - sto d'un guindo-lo, Più le - sto d'un
The fate of a big-a-mist, A tri - or - tet -
N
p
Ve - dre - mo a ri - gagnoli, Ve - dre - mo a ri -
You sym - bol of van - i - ty, We'll bring you to
M
p
E al - lor la sua fre-go-la, E al - lor la sua
Your shame less du - plic - i - ty, Will bring you pub -
Q
p
Co - sì so - glion l'i - la-ri, Co - sì so - glion
'T will take in - gen - u - i - ty And great as - sid -
FEN
Ma co - le - i che in
There I see her, so
Dr C
can - to Gen - ti son di sua tri - bù, Non son due stin - chi di
- side you: They are e - vil through and through. Let my friend - ly coun - sel
B
- sa - to Non è sal - vo che a me - tà. Tocca a voi d'or - dir l'ag -
need me. Let my warn - ing come in time. It is you who now must
FOR
- dopera L'ar - te mia con quel - l'in - fa - me; E sa - rà prez - zo del -
- os - i - ty In the way I shall en - snare him, Then the ti - ger - ish fe -
P
La mi - naccia or v'è sco - per - ta
There is noth - ing more to men - tion,

A
guindo_lo, Lo fac_cio gi_rar. Quel_l'o_tre. quel
-rag-a-mist, Is sad when you're fat! f The mon-ster, the
N
_gagno_li Quel_l'or_co su_dar. Quel_l'o_tre quel
san-i-ty, And hand you your hat. f The mon-ster, the
M
fre_go_la, Ve_dre_mo svam_par. Quel_l'o_tre quel
-lic-i-ty, We'll wa-ger on that! f The mon-ster, the
Q
l'i_la_ri Co_ma_ri ciar_lar. Quel_l'o_tre quel
-u-i-ty To bat-ter him flat. The mon-ster, the
EN
cor mi no_mi_ni,
sweet, so beau-ti-ful,
C
san_to, Nè son fio_ri di vir_tù. Ma quei due che a_ve_te ac_
guide you: I'd be-ware if I were you! The two ras-cals here be-
B
_gua_to Che l'ag_gua_to stor_ne_rà. L'uom av_vi_
heed me To pre-vent this ug-ly crime! I know you
OR
_l'ope_ra Lo sven_ta_re le sue tra_me Se da me stor_no il ri_
-roc-i-ty I'll dis-play when I shall tear him. The old ras-cal will be
P
Or v'è no_to il ciur_ma_dor, La mi_naccia or v'è sco_
Now the rest is up to you. There is noth-ing more to

A
ti - no! Quel - l'o - tre, quel
bar - rel! The mon - ster, the
N
ti - no! Quel - l'o - tre, quel
bar - rel! The mon - ster, the
M
ti - no! Quel - l'o - tre, quel
bar - rel! The mon - ster, the
Q
ti - no! Quel - l'o - tre, quel
bar - rel! The mon - ster, the
FEN
Dol - - - - ce a - mor, vuol
She whose love is
Dr. C
can - to, Gen - ti son di sua tri - bù, Non son due stin - chi di
- side you: They are e - vil through and through. Let my friend - ly coun - sel
B
- sa - to, Non è sal - vo che a me - tà, sì Toc - ca a voi d'or - dir l'ag-
need me, Let my warn - ing come in time: For it is you who now must
FOR
- di - co - lo Non a - vrem o - pra - to in - van, Se l'at - ti - ro nel - l'in-
sor - ry, For my venge-ance can-not fail, When the hunt-er turns to
P
- per - ta, Or v'è no - to il ciur - ma - dor, sì, Sta - te al - l'er - ta, al - l'er - ta, al-
men - tion, Now the rest is up to you. So be on guard and pay at -

ti - no! Ve - drai che se ab -
bar - rel! The fate of a
ti - no! E se il sci - lin -
bar - rel! You sym - bol of
ti - no! Se il vi - schio lo im -
bar - rel! Your shame-less du -
ti - no! Tal sem - pre s'e -
bar - rel! 'Twill take in - gen -
es - - - ser mi - a.
mine for - - - ev - er,
san - to, Nè son fio - ri di vir - tù.
guide you: I'd be - ware if I were you!
- gua - to Che l'ag - gua - to stor - ne - rà.
heed me To pre - vent this ug - ly crime!
- gan - no L'an - gue morde il cer - re - tan,
quar - ry And the snake will bite its tail!
l'er - ta, Qui si trat - ta del - l'o - nor.
-ten - tion And find out what he will do!

A
_bin_do_lo, Ve_drai che se ab_bin_do_lo Quel gros_so com_
big-a-mist, A tri- or tet - rag-a-mist, Is sad when you're
N
guagnolo, E se il sci_lin_guagno_lo Sa_pre_mo a_do_
van-i-ty, We'll bring you to san-i-ty, And hand you your
M
_pe_go_la, Se il vi_schio lo im_pe_go_la Lo u_dre_mo stril_
-plic-i-ty, Will bring you pub-lic-i-ty, We'll wa-ger on
Q
_si_la_ri, Tal sem_pre s'e_si_la_ri Quel bel cin_guet_
-u-i-ty And great as-sid-u-i-ty To bat-ter him
FEN
Noi sa_ _ _rem co_me due
Like an an-gel who from
Dr. C
Ma quei due che a_ve_te ac_can_to, Non son due stin_chi di
These two ras-cals here be-side you: Let my friend-ly coun-sel
B
Toc_ca a voi d'or_dir l'ag_gua_to, Toc_ca a voi d'or_dir l'ag_
Mas-ter Ford, I know you need me. It is you who now must
FOR
Se l'at_ti_ro nel_l'in_gan_no, Se l'at_ti_ro nel_l'in_
Sir John Fal-staff will be sor-ry When the hunt-er turns to
P
La mi_naccia or v'è sco_per_ta, La mi_naccia or v'è sco_
There is noth-ing more to men-tion, Be on guard and pay at-

A
N
M
Q
TEN
DR C
B
FOR
P
-par
fat!
Più le-sto d'un
Watch out, you po-
-prar, sa-pre-mo a-do-prar, Ve-dre-mo a ri-
hat. We'll hand you your hat. You sym-bol of
-lar, lo u-dre-mo stril-lar, E al-lor la sua
that, We'll wa-ger on that! Your shame-less du-
-tar, quel bel cin-guet-tar, Co-sì so-glion
flat, To bat-ter him flat. For all his fat-
ge-mi-ne stel-le
Heav-en de-scend-ed,
san-to, Nè son fio-ri di vir-tù.
guide you, They are ev-il through and through!
-gua-to Che l'ag-gua-to stor-ne-rà.
heed me To pre-vent this ug-ly crime!
-gan-no, L'angue morde il cer-re-tan.
quar-ry And the snake will bite its tail!
-per-ta, Or v'è no-to il ciur-ma-dor.
-ten-tion And find out what he will do!
3
3
3

A
guindo-lo, Più le-sto d'un guindo-lo, Più le-sto, più
-lyg-a-mist, The fate of a big-a-mist, A tri- or tet-
N
-gagno-li, Ve-dre-mo a ri-gagno-li, Quel-l'or-co, quel-
van-i-ty, We'll bring you to san-i-ty, And teach you ur-
M
fre-go-la E al-lor la sua fre-go-la Ve-dre-mo, ve-
-plic-i-ty, Will bring us fe-lic-i-ty And bring you pub-
Q
l'i-la-ri, Co-sì so-glion l'i-la-ri, Co-sì so-glion
-u-i-ty 'Twill take in-gen-u-i-ty and great as-si-
FEN
due ge-mi-ne
From Heav-en de-
Dr C
Nè son fio-ri di vir-tù.
They are e-vil through and through!
B
Toc-ca a voi, toc-ca a voi,
Mas-ter Ford, Mas-ter Ford,
FOR
Se l'at-ti-ro nel-l'in-gan-no
Sir John Fal-staff will be sor-ry
P
Sta-te al-l'er-ta sta-te al-l'er-ta
Pay at-ten-tion! Pay at-ten-tion!

le - sto, Lo fac - cio gi - rar
-rag- a -mist Is sad when you're fat!
l'or - co, quel - l'or - co su - dar
-ban- i - ty, And hand you your hat!
- dre - mo, ve - dre - mo svam - par
-lic- i - ty We'll wa - ger on that!
l'i - la - ri Co - ma - ri ciar - lar
-u - i - ty, Till we bat - ter him flat.
stel - - - - - - - le u - ni - te in
- scend - - - - - - - ed to em -
Non son due stin - chi di
Let my friend - ly coun - sel
Toc - ca a voi d'or - dir l'ag -
Mas - ter Ford, you now must
Se l'at - ti - ro nel - l'in -
When the hunt - er turns to
Sta - te al - l'er - ta, al - l'er - ta, al -
Be on guard and pay at -

PIÙ PRESTO ♩. = 126
A
N
M
Q
FEN
(All the men exit.)
un ar - dor.
- bloom my heart.
Dr C
san - to, Nè son fio - ri di vir - tù.
guide you I'd be-ware if I were you!
B
- gua - to Che l'ag-gua - to stor - ne - rà.
heed me, To pre-vent this ug - ly crime!
FOR
- gan - no L'an-gue morde il cer - re - tan.
quar - ry And the snake will bite its tail!
P
- l'er - ta, Qui si trat-ta del - l'o - nor.
- ten - tion And find out what he will do!
EXIT
PIÙ PRESTO ♩. = 126
(39)
ff
p

Qui più non si vagoli...
E- nough of this jab-bering!
(to Quickly)
Tu
'Tis
corri al-l'uf-fi - cio tuo.
time now for you to go.
Vo'ch'egli mia - go-li d'a-
He shall be howl - ing like a
- mor come un mi - cio.
cat in the moon- - light.
(to Quickly)
È in- te-sa.
You fol-low?
È
That's
Sì.
Yes.
brillante
pp

A: Do_ma_ni. / To-mor-row! — Buon dì / Good day,

N: det_ta. / splen_did.

Q: Sì. / Yes! — Sì. / Yes!

legg.

A: Meg. / Meg.

N: Ad_dio. / Good day. — Buon dì. / Good day.

M: Buon dì. / Good day. — Buon / Good

Q: Nan_net_ta, buon dì. / My An-nie, good day!

(holding the others back)

A: Ve_drai che quel_l'e_pa Ter- / We'll see how his bel_ly will

M: dì. / day.

pp e molto stacc.

A
ri - - bi-le e tronfia Si gon - - - -
soon be ex-pand-ing, and grow-
p
A
fia, si gon - - - - fia, si
NAN. -ing... and bloat - - ing, and
MEG
Si gon - - - - fia, si
and bloat - - - - ing, and
Si
and
ppp
ppp
A
gon - - fia, si gon - - - - - - -
bloat - - ing, and bloat
N
gon - - fia, si gon - - - - - - -
bloat - - ing, and bloat
M
gon - - fia, si gon - - - - - - -
QUIC. bloat - - ing, and bloat
Si gon - - - - - - -
and bloat
f

LO STESSO MOVIMENTO ♩=126
A
fia e poi cre - pa.
ing un - til it bursts!
N
fia e poi cre - pa.
ing un - til it bursts!
M
fia e poi cre - pa.
ing un - til it bursts!
Q
fia e poi cre - pa.
ing un - til it bursts!
fff
LO STESSO MOVIMENTO ♩=126
cantabile
A
(40)
Ma il vi - so mi - o su lui ri - splen - de - rà
"Your ra - diant beau - ty on me will shed its light
ppp
Co - me u - na stel
as bright and smil
NAN.
Co - me u - na stel
". . . as bright and smil
cres.

A
- la, come una stel - la sul - l'im - men - - si -
- ing out of the sky a star will shine at
N
- - la, come una stel - la sul - l'im - men - - si
MEG
- - ing out of the sky a star will shine at
Come una stel - la sul - l'im - men - - si
QUIC.
"... out of the sky a star will shine at
Come una stel - la sul - l'im - men - - si -
"... out-of the sky a star will shine at
f
dim.
tr
-tà, ah! ah! ah! ah! ah! ah! ah! ah! ah! ah! ah! ah! ah! ah! ah!
night!" Ha, ha, ha, ha, ha, ha, ha, ha, ha, ha, ha, ha, ha, ha, ha,
mf

VIVACE
(They all leave, laughing.)
A
ah!
ha!
N
ah!
ha!
M
ah!
ha!
Q.
ah!
ha!
VIVACE
ff
(curtain)

Act Two

Part One

(At the Garter Inn, as in Act One. Falstaff again seated in his armchair, drinking his sherry. Bardolph and Pistol near the door to the left.)

(singing together and pounding their chests—at each sign*—
in a gesture of contrition)
BARDOLFO
MOLTO PIÙ LENTO ♩. = 66
Siam pen_ti _ ti e con_tri _ ti.
See us sigh - ing, weak from cry - ing!
PISTOLA
Siam pen_ti _ ti e con_tri _ ti.
See us sigh - ing, weak from cry - ing!
(1)
MOLTO PIÙ LENTO ♩. = 66
(barely turning towards Bardolph and
FALSTAFF Pistol)
L'uomo ri_tor_na al vi_zio, la gatta al lar_do...
Men will re-turn to vice like mice to the lard-er.
B
E.............. noi, tor_
Let us re-
P
E.............. noi, tor_
Let us re-

I° TEMPO
_niamo al tuo ser _ vi _ _ _ zio.
-turn once more to serve you!
_niamo al tuo ser _ vi _ _ _ zio.
-turn once more to serve you!
page 153
I° TEMPO
f
dim.
(to Falstaff)
Pa_dron, là c'è u_na don_na ch'al_la
Sir John, Out - side the door there's some-one
p
vo _ stra pre_sen _ za chie _ de d'es_ser am_mes _ sa.
wait - ing, A wom - an who would like you to see her.

(Bardolph exits to the left and returns at once with Mrs. Quickly.)
FAL.
(2)
S'i - nol - tri.
I'll see her.
mf
p
marcato
QUICKLY
(curtsying deeply towards Falstaff who remains seated)
ASSAI MODERATO ♩=80
Re_ve - ren - za!
I am hon - ored.
FAL.
ASSAI MODERATO ♩=80
Buon
Ad -
p
Q
Re_ve - ren - za!
I am hon - ored.
FAL.
gior - no buo_na don - na.
-vance, my worth-y wom - an!
m.s.

(advancing cautiously)
Q
Se vo_stra grazia vuo_le, Vor_rei, se_gre_ta_
Sir John, with your per - mis - sion I shall, but most dis-
_men - te, dir_le quat_tro pa_ro_le.
FAL. creet - ly, make you a prop-o - si - tion.
T'accor_dou_
Your wish be
(curtsies again, then draws nearer to Falstaff)
(to Bardolph and Pistol who have remained in the background to listen)
Reve_ren_
I am hon_
_dien_za._ E_sci_te.
grant-ed. Pray, leave us!
p

ALL° MODERATO ♩=92
(hesitantly)
pp a bassu voce
Q
(3) _za!
-ored.
Madon_na Ali _ ce
You know a Mis-tress
ALL° MODERATO ♩=92
p
pp
f
marcato
Ford.....
Ford. . . .
(rises and turns towards Quickly, with an ambiguous smile, as if to say "Tell me more!")
Ahi_mè!
A - las!
Po _ ve _ ra
Un- hap-py
FAL.
Ebben?
I do . . . ?
pp
donna!
wom-an!
Sie_te un gran se_dut _ to _ re!
You're a bra- zen se - duc - er. . .
Lo so.
I know.
Con_
Con-
pp

Q
AL.
pp sottovoce
A_li _ ce sta in
The la - dy is
_ti _ nua.
-tin- ue!
pp
pp
gran _ de a_gi_tazio_ne d' amor per voi; vi
rav - ing with de-lir- i - ous pas-sion for you. Your
di - ce Ch'ebbe la vo _ stra let _ te_ra, che vi rin_
let - ter fills her with love and grat - i-tude. This I should

accel. un poco
Q
gra _ zia e che Suo ma _ ri _ to e _ sce sem _ _
tell you. . . And that dai-ly her hus - band is ab - -
accel. un poco
Q
_pre dal_le due al_le tre.
FAL. -sent From e-lev-en to one.
(4)
Dal_le due al_le
From e-lev-en to
p
Q
Vostra Gra_zia a quel _ l'o _ ra Po _
'Tis the time your Grace could meet her, And
FAL.
tre.
one!

Q
_trà li _ be _ ra _ men _ _ te Sa_
free of dan - ger ven - - ture in
3
Q
_lir o _ ve di _ mo_ra La bella A_
her own home to greet her. What an ad-
col canto
marcato
Q
_li ce. Po_ve_ra don_na! le ango_scie
-ven-ture! Un-hap-py wom-an! For what she
p

sottovoce
Q
su - e Son cru - de - li! ha un ma-ri-to ge-
suf - fers is in - hu - man: Mas-ter Ford is a
Q
-lo - so!
de - mon! (mulling over Quickly's remarks)
(to Quickly)
FAL.
sottovoce
ff
Dal-le due al-le tre. Le di-
. . . from e-lev-en to one! Go and
p
p
FAL.
-rai che impa - zï-en - te aspetto quel - l'o - ra.
tell her that my heart is ach-ing to see her.
p

Q
Ben det_to.
I bless you.
AL.
Al mio dover non manche_rò.
My du-ty tells me what to do!
parlando
Q
Ma c'è un' al_tra amba_
There is still one more
Q
_scia_ta per Vo_stra Gra_zia.
mes-sage I am to bring you. . . .
FAL.
dolce
Par_la.
Tell me!
(5)

cantando
Q
La bel _ la Meg (un
This one from Meg (an
LARGO ♩. = 56
an _ _ ge _ lo che innamora a guar _ dar _ la) An _
an _ _ gel whom to be-hold is to wor _ ship!) She,
LARGO ♩. = 56
ppp leggerissimo
I° TEMPO ♩ = 92
_ ch'es _ sa vi sa _ lu _ ta mol _ _ _ to amo _ ro _ sa _
too, has asked me to as _ sure you of her great
I° TEMPO ♩ = 92
_ men _ te, Di _ ce che suo ma _ ri _ to è as _
ar _ dor. She has a-spouse who all the time stays
f

_sai di ra _ do as _ sen_te..... Po _ ve _ ra
in the house to guard her. Un - hap - py
p
COME PRIMA
donna! un gi _ _ glio di can_dore e di
wom-an! As white as snow is her in - no-cent
COME PRIMA
ppp
morendo
fè!...........
heart!
8
pp
morendo

ALL°. VIVO ♩ = 126

Q

f

Voi le strega _ te tutte.
No-one es-capes your mag-ic.

FAL.

portando

Stregoneria non c'è Ma un
I cast no mag - ic spell. And

(6)

ALL°. VIVO ♩ = 126

mf *p*

cantando

FAL

cer - to qual mio fa_sci_no per_so_
yet I wield a cer-tain charm of my

FAL

_nal.... Dim - mi:
own. Tell me:

brillante

allarg. un poco
Oi - bò! La don-na na-sce
Of course! No wom-an tells an-
l'al-tra sa di que-st'al-tra?
Each one keeps her own se-cret?
p col canto
a tempo
scal - tra. Non te-me-te.
-oth - er... not in this case.
(searching his purse)
Or ti
You have
p legg.
a tempo
Chi se - mi - na
Who sow - eth his
vo' re - mu - ne - rar...
earned a just re - ward.

Q
Gra - zie, racco - glie a - mor.
fa - vors shall har - vest love.
(offering her a small coin)
FAL
Pren - di, Mercu - - rio-
Take this, you fe - - male
FAL
-fe-mi-na.
Mer-cu-ry!
cres.
(dismissing her with a gesture)
COME PRIMA
FAL
Sa - lu - ta le due
Be sure to greet my
COME PRIMA
pp

(exits to the left)
M'in - chi - - no.
Your serv - - ant!
da - me.
la - dies!
pp
p
pp
allarg. e marcato
(7)
(A - li - ce è
(She's mine! I've
ALL°. SOSTENUTO = 100
mi - a!)
won her!)
ALL°. SOSTENUTO = 100
ff

FAL.
Va..., vec-chio John, va,
Go, gal-lant John, go,
pp
FAL
va per la tua vi - - a.
go on-ward to glo - - ry!
marcate
Que-sta tua vec-chia
You, might-y mound of
FAL
car-ne an - co - ra spre - - - - me
mat-ter, once more shall ren - - - - der
f
FAL
Qual-che dolcez - za a te.
Your gen - - 'rous help to me.
dolce
p
f
Tut-te le
Wom-en are

don - ne ammu-ti-na-te in-sie-me Si dan-na-no per
haunt - ed by your spa-cious splen-dor, As an - y - one can
p
p
me! Buon cor - - - po di Sir
see. My paunch, at last I
pp
John, ch'io nu-tro e sa - zio, Va, ti rin-gra - zio.
know why I should feed you. Thanks! I shall need you.
p

(8)
ALL°. COME PRIMA ♩ = 100
ff
(entering from the left)
BAR.
RECIT. prestissimo
Padron; di là c'è un cer_to Mastro Fonta_na Che a_ne_la di co-
Sir John, I bring a mes-sage from a Mas-ter Brook Who wants to have a
col canto
B
_noscervi; offre u_na da_migiana di Cipro per l'asciolvere di Vostra Signo_
word with you; he of-fers you a dem- i-john of Cy-prus to as-sure you of a pleas-ant

ri - a
morn - ing.
Sì.
Yes.
FAL..
Il suo no - me è Fon - ta - - na?
And this Brook, is he here now?
p
mf
ALLEGRO ♩= 132
Be - ne ac - col - ta si - a La fon -
I am fond of brooks that run so
ALLEGRO ♩= 132
ppp
ta - - na che span - - de un si - mi - le li -
free - - ly, whose flow be - speaks - such - tast - y
cres.
quo - - re!
tid - - ings.
En - tri.
He's wel - come!
f

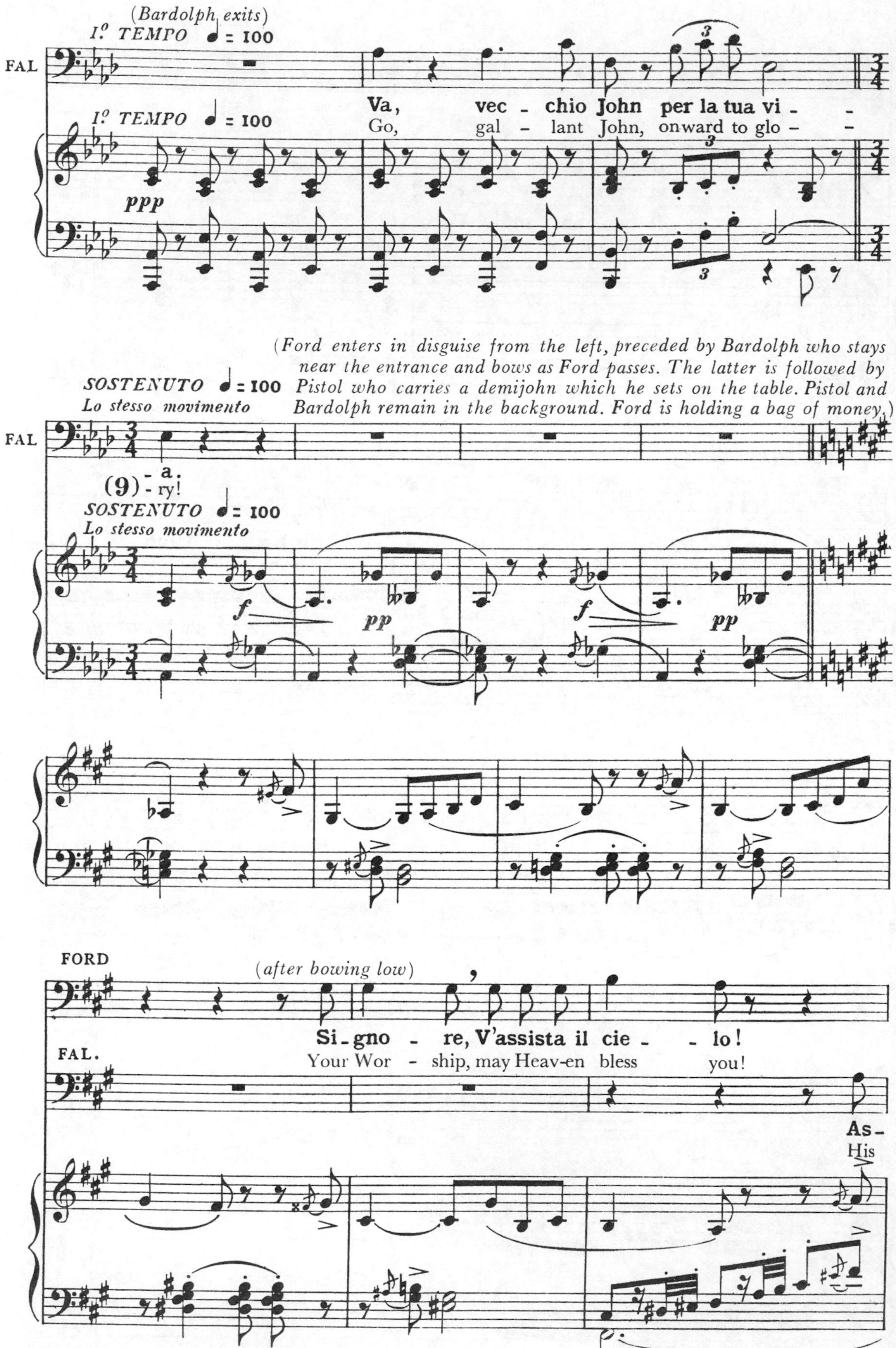

(Ford enters in disguise from the left, preceded by Bardolph who stays near the entrance and bows as Ford passes. The latter is followed by Pistol who carries a demijohn which he sets on the table. Pistol and Bardolph remain in the background. Ford is holding a bag of money.)

SOSTENUTO ♩= 100
Lo stesso movimento

FAL

- a.
(9) - ry!

SOSTENUTO ♩= 100
Lo stesso movimento

f pp f pp

FORD

(after bowing low)

Si-gno - re, V'assista il cie - lo!
Your Wor - ship, may Heav-en bless you!

FAL.

As-
His

(respectfully)
Io sono, dav - ver, mol - to in - di -
As I am a - ware, my bold in -
(returning the greeting)
- si - sta voi pur, si - gno - re.
mer - cy may be on you, Sir!
m.s.
- scre - to, e vi chie - do per - do - no, Se,.......
- tru - sion —with your kind - ly fore - bear - ance— seems
..... senza ce - ri - mo - nie, qui ven - go e sprovve -
to be quite ill man - nered, an in - so - lent pre -

FOR
-du - to Di più lunghi pre_ambo_li.
-sump - tion, as a gen-tle-man ought to know.
FAL.
Voi siete il ben_ve_
You could not be more
ALL°. MODERATO ♩= 100
Lo stesso movimento
FAL
-nu - - - to
wel - - come!
(10)
ALL°. MODERATO ♩= 100
Lo stesso movimento
mf
pp
pp
FOR.
In me vede_te un uomch'ha un'ab_bon_
In me you see a man who lives in
p

-dan - za gran-de
wealth and boun-ty,
Degli a-gi del-la vi - ta;............
Whose ev-ery wish is grant - ed.
p
un uom che spen-de e span-de Co-me
A man who lends and spends and nev-er
f
più gli ta-len-ta pur............
cared, nev-er count-ed, Sir,
f
pur di pas-
I shall no
ff
p
-sar mat-ta - na.
long - er bore you:
Io mi chia-mo Fon-
Mas-ter Brook stands be-

♩= 100
FOR
-ta-na!
-fore you.
(shaking his hand most cordially)
FAL.
Ca - ro si-gnor Fon-ta - na!
Good Mas-ter Brook, I greet you.
Voglio fa-re con
From the first you have
♩= 100
mf
p
(expansively)
FOR
Ca - ro Sir
Gal - lant Sir
FAL
voi più am-pia co-no-scen-za.
made a most pro-found im-pres-sion.
p
FOR
John de-si-de-ro par-lar-vi in con-fi -
John, I trust I may have faith in your dis -

LO STESSO MOV.to
-den-za.
BAR. -cre-tion.
(whispering to Pistol, both hiding in the background)
(At-ten-to! Guar-da! Scom-
(At-ten-tion! Watch it! How
PIS.
(softly to Bardolph)
(Zit-to!
(Qui-et!)
(11)
LO STESSO MOV.to
pp
TO ACT II PART 2
p235
-met-to! E-gli va drit-to nel tra-boc-chet-to.
wil-y! You can't de-ny it... he does it sly-ly!
pp
FAL.
(to Bardolph and Pistol) ff
Che fa-te
Are you still
Zit-to!
Qui-et!
PIS.
Ford se lo in-trappola
Net-ting the but-ter-fly!
Zit-to!)
Qui-et!)

(Bardolph and Pistol reluctantly withdraw.)
(to Ford)
FAL
là!
here?
V'a-
Con-
ff
senza misura, presto
spoken
FOR
Sir John, m'infonde ardi-re Un ben noto proverbio po-po-lar:
Sir John, will you al-low me to re-sort to a wise and an-cient saw:
FAL
-scol-to.
- tin-ue!
ALL.º MODERATO ♩= 100
(long silence)
FOR
Si suol di-re Che l'o-ro a-pre ogni por-ta, Che
ALL.º MODERATO ♩= 100
"When the key is of gold, no lock will re-sist it." To
lunga pausa
ff
FOR
l'o-ro è un ta-li-sma-no, Che l'o-ro vin-ce tut-to.
gold and all its splen-dor, To gold they all sur-ren-der.
pp

FAL.
L'o - - ro è un buon ca-pi-ta - no Che mar - cia a -
Gold will con-quer the world, proud - ly march - ing
f
p
FOR. (approaching the table)
Eb - bene.... Ho un sac - co di mo -
Pre - cise-ly! Per - chance I find this
- van - ti.
on-ward.
(12)
p
- ne - te Qua, che mi pe-sa as-sai. Sir
bag of gold weighs too much for me. Sir
f

FOR
John........ se voi vo - le - te A - iu - tar - mi a por - tar - lo?...
John, may I im - pose up - on your kind - ness to help me?
FAL.
Con gran pia -
Of course I
(taking the bag and placing it on the table)
FAL
- cer...
shall!
non so, Dav - ver,
But may I know
FOR.
Ve lo di - rò...
You may in - deed.
C'è a
In
FAL
per qual mio me - ri - to, Mes - se - re....
why it is I whom you have chos - en. . . .

ANDANTE ♩=69
Wind_sor u_na da_ma, bel_la e leg_gia_dra
Wind_sor lives a la-dy, love-ly, de-mure, and
ANDANTE ♩=69
(13)
mol_to, Si chiama A_li_ce; è mo_glie d'un cer_to
haunt-ing. Her name is A-lice, her hus-band a cer-tain
pp stacc.
Ford....
Ford.
Io
I
FAL.
V'a_scol_to.
En-chant-ing.

LO STESSO MOVIMENTO ♩= 69
FOR
l'a - mo e lei non m'ama; le scri - vo, non ri -
woo her, can-not sub-due her; Im - plore her, seem to
LO STESSO MOVIMENTO ♩= 69
tr
p
FOR
- sponde; La guar - do, non mi guarda; la
bore her; Be - seech her, can-not reach her; Pur -
tr
legato
con espress.
poco string. ♩= 120
FOR
cer - co e si na-sconde. Per lei spre - cai te -
- sue her . . . can-not get to her! In des - per - ate de -
poco string. ♩= 120
tr
f
FOR
- so - ri, git - tai do - ni su
- lu - sion, to show that I a -

do - ni, E-sco-gi-tai,.................... tre -
-dore her. In un-re-strained pro-

man - do, il vol del-le oc-ca -
fu - sion I spread. my wealth be -

dim.

sempre stacc.

sio - ni. Ahi-mè! tut - to fu
fore her. A-las! all this was

p

va-no!... Ri-ma-si sul-le sca-le, Ne-
use-less! A cast-a-way cru-sad-er, I

FOR
_glet_to, a bocca a_sciut - ta, cantando un madri -
floun-der and fly a - round her, And sad-ly ser - e -
a piacere
leggerissimo
pp dim. sempre ed allarg.
FOR
_ga - - - - - - - - - - - - - -
_nade
LO STESSO MOVIMENTO = 120
FOR
- - _le.
her!
FAL.
(gaily)
L'a - mor, l'a - mor che non ci
I know, I know that love is
LO STESSO MOVIMENTO = 120
(14)
p

imitando
strug - ge
. . . taunt you
dà mai tre - - gue Fin-chè la vi-ta strug - ge. È
blessed and blight - - ed, how love will twit and taunt you, and
che chi fug-ge...
. . . it will haunt you . . .
co - - - me l'om - bra... in-
like a shad - ow . . . you
legg.
E chi l'in - se-gue... l'a-
. . . and as you fight it . . . You
- se-gue... fug - ge,
fight it . . . 'twill haunt you!

con forza
FOR
mor, l'a - mor! E
know . . . . . . my woe . . . To
FAL
l'a - mor, l'a - mor!
Quite so! I know!
mf
FOR
que - - - sto ma - dri - ga - le l'ho ap -
suf - - - fer and to lan - guish I've
mf
FOR
- pre - so a prez - zo d'or.
FAL
paid my weight in gold.
Que - st'è il destin fa -
The am - a - to - ry
f

cantarellando
L'a - -
I
- ta - le del mi - se-ro ama - tor.
an - guish will tor - ture young and' old!
pp
- mor, l'a - - - mor che non ci
know 'tis so! What can we
dà mai tre - - - - - - gue...
do to fight it....
FAL
Es - sa non vi
And not e - ven

FOR
FAL
No.
No.
dié' mai luo-go a lu - sin-ghe? Ma in-
once she seemed to be yield-ing? But
p
pp
SEMPRE LO STESSO MOVIMENTO ♩=120
come prima
Ve lo di - rò:
Let me ex - plain:
- fin, perchè v'apri - te a me?
why pour out your heart to me?
SEMPRE LO STESSO MOVIMENTO ♩=120
(15)
f
Voi sie-te un gen - ti - luo-mo
You are a man of bear-ing,

pro - de, ar - gu - to, fa - con - do,
no - ble, well-spok - en, and cun - ning,
pp
f
p
Voi sie - te un uom di guer - ra, voi sie - te un uom di
A man of fear - less dar - ing whose gal - lant - ry is
f
ff
p
mondo... Non v'a - du - lo, e quel - lo è un sacco di mo -
stun - ning. I am se - rious. My gold shall serve to make you
FAL. (humbly)
Oh!
...Well...
ppp

FOR
-ne - te: Spen - - de - - te-le! spen-
hap - py: A - - way with it! Go
f
FOR
-de - - te-le! sì, spen - de - - te e span -
play with it! You shall spend and ex -
stacc.
FOR
-de - te Tut - to il mio pa - tri -
-spend it, You shall cher - ish and be -
FOR
-mo - nio! Sia - te ric - - - - -
-friend it, you shall live
f

R
co e fe - li - ce!
in its splen-dor!
Ma, in contrac -
All I am
p
R
dolce
- cambio,
ask-ing
chie - do che con-qui-stia-te A - li -
is that to you she must sur - ren -
pp
R
- ce!
- der.
Mi spiego:
Quite sim-ply:
FAL.
Strana ingiunzion!
What do you mean?
leggero

ALL°. MOD.to ♪ = 112
FOR
Quel-la crudel bel - tà Sempre è vis - su-ta in gran-de fe - de di
My love-ly ice-berg prides her-self On be-ing thought a par-a-gon of
ALL°. MOD.to ♪ = 112
(16) mf
allarg.................... poco più animato
FOR
ca - sti - tà. La sua vir-tu im-por-tu - - na m'ab-
chas - ti - ty. Her vir-tu-ous de-mean - - or has
poco più animato
allarg.................... mf
leggero
FOR
-bar-ba-glia-va gl'oc - chi, La bel-la i-ne-spu-gna-bi-le di-
made my pas-sion keen - er. Her eyes will tell the world for all to
(in falsetto)
Cantabile
FOR
-cea: Guai se mi toc - chi! Ma se
see: "No - one come near me!" But if
col canto
pp
p

LO STESSO MOVIM.to ♩ = 112
pp
OR
voi l'e - - spu - gna - te, poi,........................
you, Sir, should win her, I,
LO STESSO MOVIM.to ♩ = 112
pp
OR
.... posso anch'io spe - rar; Da fal - lo na - sce
in due time, may, too: One fall makes her a
allarg.
(long silence)
FOR
fal - - lo e al - lor... Che ve ne par?
sin - - ner and then . . . is this not true?
ALL.o
FAL.
3
Prima di
Now to be -
lunga pausa

ALL°. AGITATO 𝅗𝅥 = 66
FAL
tut - to, senza compli - menti, Messe - - - - re Accetto il
-gin and ex-pe-dite the mat-ter I shall ac-cept your
ALL°. AGITATO 𝅗𝅥 = 66
(17)
sacco. Poi (fe - de di ca - va - lie - re; Qua la
mon-ey. Then (here is my hand up - on it You may
(shaking Ford's hand)
ma - no!) fa - rò le vostre bra - me sa - zie. Voi, la
trust me!) your pain and trou ble shall be end - ed. You shall
FOR.
Gra - zie!!
Splen - did!
moglie di Ford pos - se - de - re - te. Io
win Mis-tress Ford, she will sur - ren - der! I'm

L
son già mol-to in - nan - zi; (non c'è ra - gion ch'io tac - cia Con
well a - long my way, Sir, (Why should I hide my se - cret from
p
AL
voi)
you?)
fra u - na mez - z'o - ra sa -
This ver - y day, Sir, I
FOR.
(surprised, half choking)
Chi?...
Whom?
(calmly)
AL
- rà nel-le mie brac-cia.
swear I shall em- brace her!
A - li - - ce.
Your la - - dy,
dolce
p
fff
p

sottovoce
ppp
FAL
Es-sa mandò di - an - - - zi u-na... confi-
Some-one she sent to me this morn-ing to en-
FAL
-den - te Per dir-mi che quel tan-ghe-ro di suo ma-
-treat me, has told me that the sim - ple-ton she calls a
cres.
f
FAL
-ri-to è as-sen - - te Dalle due alle
hus-band is ab - - sent from e-lev-en to
f
p
FOR.
Dal-le due al-le tre... Lo co-no-sce-te?
From e-lev-en to one! Pray, do you know him?
FAL
tre. Il
one. For

L
dia - vo - lo Se lo por-ti al-l'in-fer-no con..........
all I care may he sim-mer-in Hell and choke
(18)
f
ff
AGITATO ♩= 120
..........Me-ne-lao suo a-vo-lo! Quel
on his own stu-pid-i-ty! That
AGITATO ♩= 120
pp stacc.
tanghero, quel tanghero, vedrai, ve-
sim-ple-ton, that ad-dle-head, The scamp, the
-drai, vedrai, vedrai, vedrai! Te lo cor-ni-fi-co netto,
fool, the lout, I'll cast him out, make him horn-if-er-ous, neat-ly,
p
f

FAL
net_to! Se mi fra_
sweet-ly! Should he be
_stor - - na Gli spa - ro u - na gi - -
mul - - ish I'll show him how to
pp
_ran - do - la di bot - te sul - le
crown his brow and e - ven seem more
f
cor - na! Quel messer Ford è un
fool - ish! Ford is a cow, a
f
ff

bu - e, un bu - e, un bu -
bull - ock! He's moo - ing and chew -
- e, un bu - e! Vedrai! Te lo cor
- ing and boo - ing. Watch out how I shall
- bello, vedrai, te lo cor - bello, vedrai, vedrai, vedrai,
twit him! No doubt I shall out-wit him. The lout, I clout his snout,
Te lo cor - ni - fi - co net - to
Make him horn - if - er - ous, neat - ly,

FAL
net - to! Quel tanghero, quel tanghero, quel tanghero, quel
sweet - ly. That sim-ple-ton, I'll bet-ter him, that vag - a -bond, I'll
ff
ff
FAL
tan - ghe - ro!
fet - ter him!
f
Ma è
You
allarg. a piacere
FAL
tar - di. Aspettami qua. Va - do a far - mi
wait here un-til I re - turn, har-nessed in grace and
ppp leggero
(19)
col canto
(Falstaff takes the bag of money and exits through the door in the back. Ford remains alone.)
FAL
bel - lo.
beau - ty!
f

mf
pp
FOR.
UN POCO PIÙ MOD.to ♩= 108
È so-gno? o re-al-
A night-mare . . . an e-vil
UN POCO PIÙ MOD.to ♩= 108
ppp
-tà...
dream?
p
Due
A
ppp
pp
sottovoce
ra-mi e-nor-mi Cre-scon sul-la mia te - sta. È un
mon-strous fork is grow-ing out of my fore - head! A
pp
f
dim.

ALL.° AGITATO ♩= 120
FOR
so - gno?... (20)
night - mare?
ALL.° AGITATO ♩= 120
Ma-stro
Mas-ter
ppp
p
cres.
Ford! Mastro Ford!
Ford, Mas-ter Ford
Dor - mi?
. . . a- wak - en,
cres.
Svegliati! Su!.. ti de-sta! Tua moglie
rouse your-self, look and lis-ten! Your wife is
f
f
sgarra e mette in mal'as-setto L' onor tuo, la tua
stray-ing . . . her scan-dal-ous flir-ta-tion Will go on to a-

FOR
ca_sa ed il tuo let - - to!
-dul-t'ry and deg-ra-da - - tion!
ff
dim.
morendo
FOR.
LO STESSO MOV.to ♩= 120
cupo
L'o - ra e fis - sa - ta,
LO STESSO MOV.to ♩= 120
Planned with af - fec-tion
p
p
FOR
trama - to l'inganno;
and timed to per-fec-tion!

sempre p
FOR
Sei gabba - to e truf - fa - to!..
Go and try to pre - vent it!
(21)
allarg. ♩=80
con espansione
FOR
E poi di - ran - no...... Che un ma - ri - to ge - loso è un in - sensa -
And yet they'll tell me That a man who is jeal - ous is de - ment -
allarg. ♩=80
f
a tempo ♩=120
FOR
- to!
-ed!
a tempo ♩=120
p
FOR
Già dietro a me no - mi d'in - fa - me
All o - ver town I hear them taunt and

FOR
co - nio Fi - schian pas - san - do; mor - mo - ra lo
jeer me, Whis - p'ring their in - sults, whis - tling when they're
scherno.
near me.
O ma - tri - mo - nio: In -
Mar - - - - - - riage is trea - - son in -
(22)
p
f
- fer - - - - no!
- fer - - - - nal.
f

FOR
Don - na: De - mo - - - - - nio!
Tor - ment e - ter - - - - - - nal!
f
FOR
Nel_la lor
Ah, what a
ff
FOR
moglie abbian fe_de i bab_be_i!
fool, he who trusts in a wom-an!
p
ff
FOR
Af.fide - rei La mia birra a un Te - desco,
I should en - trust my cham-pagne to a French-man
pp
ff
fp

OR
Tut_to il mio
Or ask a
pp
fp
OR
desco a un O_lan_de_se lur_co,
Dutch-man to pa_trol my pan_try,
pp
ff
FOR
La mia bot_ti.glia d'acqua.vi_te a un
I'd trust a scoun-drel with-out name or
pp
FOR
Tur_co, Non
gen-try But
mia mo_glie a sè
no wife and her
ff
pp

FOR
stes_sa.-
vir-tue!
O lai - da
Oh fright, oh
FOR
sor_te! Quella brutta pa - ro - la in cor mi
sor-row! I re-mem-ber the words he spoke to
(shouting)
FOR
tor - na: Le cor - na! Bu - e! Ca-
warn me: "The horns, Sir!" Hor-ror . . . 'tis
(23)
pp
f
mf
FOR
-pron! Le fu_sa tor - te! Ah! le cor_na! le
true . . . May-be to-mor-row . . . Ah, they're grow-ing, they're

cor - na!
show - ing!
Ma.......... non mi sfug.gi -
Ah, I will take re -
-rai! no! sozzo, re.o, Dan.na - - to e.pi.cu -
-venge! You snip-er . . . swip-er . . . You God - - for-sak-en
-re - o! Pri - - ma li ac -
vi - per! First I'll a -
-cop.pio E poi li col - go, li ac - cop.pio, li
-bet them, then I shall fret them, Be - set them, and

FOR
col - go, li ac-cop-pio, li
net them . . . A - bet them, then
colgo, li accoppio, li colgo, li colgo, li ac-
fret them, be-set them and get them and finally
cres.
cres. sempre
FOR
- cop - pio!
net them!
(choking)
Io
Yes,
ff
pp
FOR
scop - pio!
net them!
FOR
ppp
morendo

(violently)
Molto più lento ♩=80
pp
Vendiche_rò l'af_fronto! Lau_
I shall a-venge my hon-or! Come
(24) Molto più lento ♩=80
pp
f
pp
_da_ta sem_pre si_ _a Nel fon_do del mio
tri-umph or per-di- -tion, I thank my guid-ing
pp
pp
cor.................. la ge_lo_si_ _ _a.
star for my sus-pi- -cion!
ff

pp
dim.
pp
(Falstaff returns through the door in the background, dressed up in a new vest, wearing a hat and carrying a cane.)
FAL.
Eccomi
Shall we pro-
p
pp
FAL
qua. - ceed?
Son pronto. I'm ready.
pp
M'ac You'll
FORD
Vi met - to sul - la
I could not bear to
FAL
- com - pa - - gna - - te un tratto?
take me on my way, Sir?
pp

(They start to leave. Near the door they stop, each one motioning to the other
R
vi_a.
stay, Sir.
FORD
to be the first to leave.)
Prima voi.
Af - ter you. . .
FAL.
Prima voi.
If you please . . .
No, no.
No, no!
pp leggero
AL
So_ _no in ca_ sa mi_ _a.
You're my guest, re - mem- -ber!
Pas_
I
pp
p
FORD
Pre_ _go...
You first!
AL
_sa_ _te.
pray you!
È tar_di. L'appuntamento
A la - dy should nev-er be kept
legato
pp

FOR
Non fa_te compli_menti...
On this there's no de-bat-ing.
Prego!
Please, Sir!
FAL
preme.
wait-ing.
Passa_te!
I beg you!
passate!
I'll fol-low!
p
(They leave together, arm in arm.)
FOR
prego!
Nev-er!
a piacere
pas_sia_mo in_sie - me!
Two-friends u - nit - ed!
FAL
Eb_ben;..
Well then . . .
pas_sia_mo in_sie - me!
two friends u - nit - ed!
col canto
(25)
ff
COME PRIMA
ff
(curtain)

Act Two

Part Two

A room in Ford's house.

A large window in the back through which we look out into the garden. Two doors, one to the left and one to the right. A third door leading to the stairway in the background, to the right. A folded screen leaning against the wall to the left, near a large fireplace. A cupboard on the right. A small table. A chest. Along the walls an armchair and several other chairs. On the armchair a lute. Flowers on the table.

A
-men - to, sulla gente gras - - - - - sa.
QUICKLY tax on peo-ple fat and port - - - - -ly.
(entering from the door at the right, laughing)
Co - My
(running towards her, as does Meg, while Ann, entering simultaneously, stays aside, obviously unhappy.)
Eb - ben? So soon?
MEG
Che c'è? The news?
Q
-ma - ri! la - dies!
Sa - rà scon - fit - to! Could not be bet-ter!
A
Bra - va! Real - ly?
Be - ne! Splen-did!
M
Be - ne! Splen - did!
Q
Fra poco gli fa - rem la festa! Our gal-lant knight will be un - seat-ed . . .
tr

Piom - bò nel lac - cio a ca - po
John Fal - staff ut - ter - ly de -
tr
f
ALI.
Narrami tutto, le - sta. Lesta.
What happened! Come and tell us! Tell us!
MEG
Lesta.
Tell us!
fit - - to.
-feat - - ed!
f
ANDANTE ♩ = 66
Giunta all'Al - bergo della Giarrettie - - ra Chiedo d'esser am-
Step-ping in-side the Garter Inn to greet him I con-veyed my re-
ANDANTE ♩ = 66
(27)
p

poco più animato
Q
-messa alla presen-za del Cava-lier, se-gre-ta mes-sag-ge-ra. Sir John si
-spects, on-ly to men-tion That I was sent by some-one else to greet him. Sir John at
mf poco più animato
(in a ponderous tone)
Q
de-gna d'accordarmi u-dien-za, M'acco-glie tron-fio in fur-fante-sca
once lent me his kind at-ten-tion. His wel-come tru-ly be-spoke his vast di-
p
COME PRIMA ♩ = 80
(imitating Falstaff)
(imitating herself)
Q
po-sa: «Buon gior-no buona donna» «Reve-ren-
-men-sion: "Ad-vance, my wor-thy wom-an"... "I am hon-
COME PRIMA ♩ = 80
pp
(28)
p

_za» A lui m'in_chi - no molto ossequï_o _ sa _ men -
-ored". I curt-sied deep - ly in my most ob-se-quious man -
pp
PIÙ MOSSO ♩ = 132
_te, poi passo alle noti_zie ghiotte. Lui beve grosso ed ogni
-ner. Then I pro-ceed-ed to en-snare him, a will-ing vic-tim. I saw him
PIÙ MOSSO ♩ = 132
mf
m.s.
mia mas_sic _ cia frot'_to _ la in _ ghiot _ te.
pick and lick the can - dy - stick I gave— him.

LO STESSO MOVIMENTO ♩ = 132
Q
In-fin, per farla spic-cia, vi cre-de en-tram-be innamo-ra-te
In short, Sir Falstaff's haugh-ti-ness Is cer-tain of your naugh-ti-ness, And sure that for his
LO STESSO MOVIMENTO ♩ = 132
pp leggerissimo e stacc.
Q
(to Alice)
cot-te Del-le bel-lez-ze su-e. E lo ve-dre-te
beau-ty You will for-get your du-ty. So be pre-pared to
ALI.
Quan-do?
Heav-ens!
Q
pre-sto, pre-sto, presto ai vo-stri piè. Og-gi,
see him at your knees this ver-y day! Sure-ly!
mf

(looking at the clock)
MEG
Son già le
I is now e -
Dal_le du_e al_le tre,
From e - lev - en to one?
qui, dal_le du_e al_le tre.
Now . . . from e - lev - en to one!
(29)
du - e! Dal_le du_e al_le tre.
-lev - en.. From e - lev-en to one!
Dal_le du_e alle tre.
From e - lev-en to one.
dal_le du_e al_le
From e - lev-en to
(hurrying to the door and calling outside)
O - là! Ned!
Come here, Ned!
tre, dal_le du_e alle tre, dal_le du_e al_le tre!
one, from e - lev-en to one, from e - lev-en to one!
cres.
stacc.

LO STESSO MOVIMENTO ♩ = 126
(to Quickly)
(calling back to the outside)
A
Will!
Già tutto ho prepa - ra_to.
Por_
Will!
I've cleared the deck for ac-tion.
Bring
LO STESSO MOVIMENTO ♩ = 126
p
pp
A
_ ta_te qua la cesta del bu - ca - to.
QUIC.
in the bas-ket ready for the laun - dry!
Sa_
We'll
p
(30)
(to Ann)
A
Nan_netta,
e tu non
My good-ness!
You are so
Q
_ rà un af_fa_re gaio!
drive him to dis - trac-tion.

ri - di?
se - rious.
Che co - s'hai?
Tell me why!
espressivo
p
Tu pian - gi?..
You're weep - ing.
Che cos'hai?
Tell me why!
Dillo a tua madre,
Come, tell your moth - er!
Eb - ben?
Go on!
Eb - ben?
Speak up!
NANNETTA (sobbing)
Mio padre...
My fath - er. . .
mio pa - dre...
My fath - er . . .
mio pa - dre...
My fath - er

A
N
A quel pe
That dod-d'ring
(breaking out in tears)
Vuo _ le........... ch'io mi ma _ ri _ ti al Dottor Ca _ jo!!...........
told me That I should mar-ry Doc-tor Ca - jus!
f
p
_dan _ te?!
dan - dy?
A quel grullo!
. . . scab-by mill-fox?
A quel bi _ sa _ vo-
. . . so thin and un - der-
M
A quel gonzo!
That old pill-box?
Q
Oi _ bò!
Good Lord!
ff

No! No! No, no, no, no!
No! No! No, no, no, no!
-lo! No, no, no, no! Piut-to-sto
-weight! No, no, no, no! I'd rath-er
No, no, no, no, no, no!
No, no, no, no, no, no!
No, no, no, no, no, no!
No, no, no, no, no, no!
Da una mi-traglia di torsi di ca- - - vo-
. . . or be shot dead by a vol-ley of pome- - - gran-
la-pi-da-ta viva...
drown or die of fe-ver!
(31)
p

A
N
M
Q
_lo.
-ate!
Non te _ mer.
Have no fear!
(jumping with joy)
Ev_
Ah,
Brava!
Real-ly!
Ben detto!
No ques-tion!
p
(Two servants have brought a basket filled with linen and other objects to be laundered.)
vi_va! Col Dottor Ca_jo non mi spo - se_
thank you! Dear Doc-tor Ca - jus, my re - ply is
ALI: (to the servants) senza misura Presto
Mettete là. Poi, quando avrò chiamato, Vuotere_te la cesta nel fos_
Put it down here. As soon as I shall call you, you will emp-ty the bas-ket in-to the
_rò!
no!
col canto

(to Ann, then to the servants about to leave)
_sa_to. Ta_ci. An _da_te.
riv-er. Qui-et! Be read-y!
Bum! Che bombarda _men _to.
Splash! What a might-y tum ble!
a tempo
f
col canto
a tempo
ff
ALI.
Prepa_ria_mo la scena.
Let's pre-pare the a-re-na!
(32)
mf
(picks up a chair and sets it near the table)
p
pp legg.
ALI.
(bringing the lute from the armchair and putting it on the table)
Qua una se_dia.
Here the chair.

NAN.
Qua il mio liu_to.
Here my lute!
ALI.
(Ann and Meg open the screen and place it between the basket and the fire-place.)
A _ priamo il pa_ra _ven_to.
The screen we bet_ter o_pen.
ALI.
Bra _ vis_si_me! Co_
Just put it there like
p

_ sì!
this!
Più a_perto an_
A lit - tle
_ co _ ra,
wid - er!
pp
a piacere
ALLEGRO ♩. = 108
Fra po_co s'inco _ mincia la com _ media'
The stage is set, the com - e - dy has start-ed.
ALLEGRO ♩. = 108
(33)
pp
pp
pp

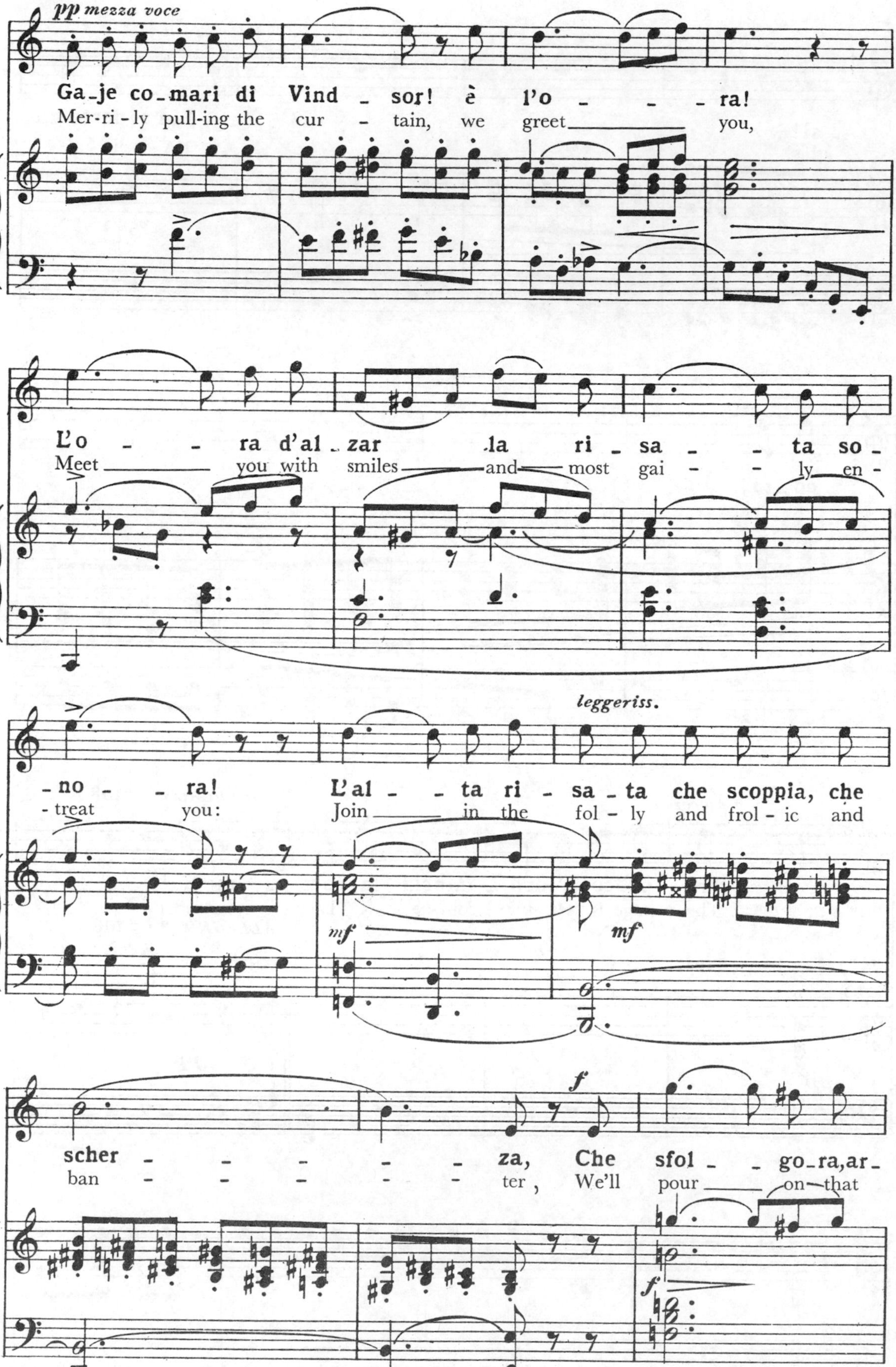

ALI.

pp mezza voce

Ga_je co_mari di Vind _ sor! è l'o _ _ ra!

Mer-ri-ly pull-ing the cur - tain, we greet you,

A

L'o - - ra d'al_zar la ri_sa - - ta so-

Meet you with smiles and most gai - - ly en-

leggeriss.

A

-no - - ra! L'al - - ta ri - sa - ta che scoppia, che

-treat you: Join in the fol - ly and frol - ic and

mf *mf*

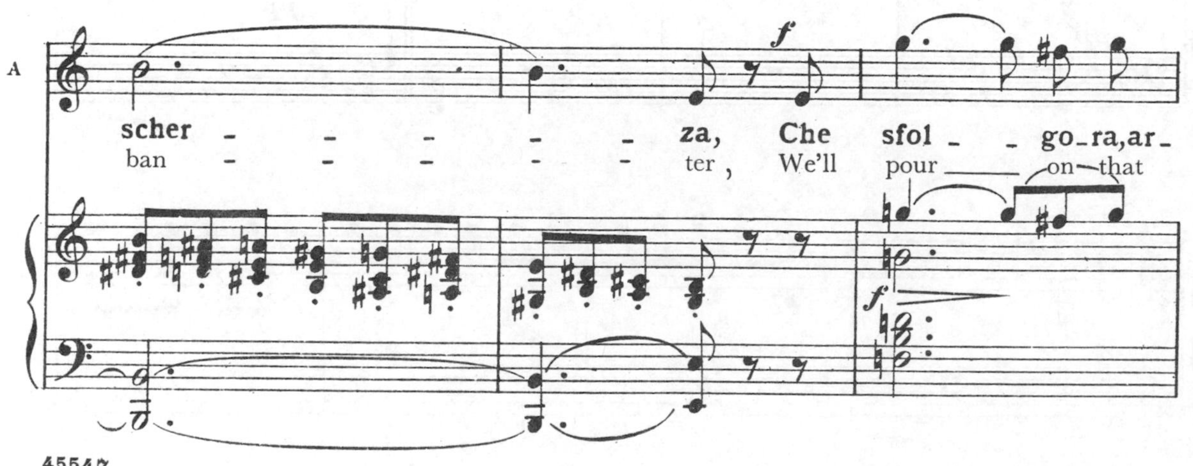
A
f
scher - - - - - za, Che sfol _ _ go_ra,ar_
ban - - - - - ter, We'll pour on that
f

A
_ma _ ta di dar _ _ di e di sferza!
jol _ ly and fool _ _ ish en _ chant-er!
(34)
pp
Ga_ie co _ ma _ _ ri! fe _ sto _ _ sa bri _
See how we beat him with lanc _ _ es of
_ga _ ta! Sul lie_to vi _ so spunti il sor _ ri _ so Splenda del
laugh _ ter, See how we cheat him, How we de _ f him, how we de _
molto stacc.
f
ppp
ri_so l'a_cu_to ful_gor!.......... Fa_vil _ _ la, fa_villa incen _
-lete him and tear him a _ part! Yet all that is done Will on_ly be

A
diaria di gio-ia nel-l'a - - - ria, Di gio - ia........
fun And make all of us hap - - - py in mind and
ne! cor.
in heart.
(35) legg.
A
But
ppp
f
noi! -
now ...
(to Meg)
Tu la parte fa-rai che ti spetta.
You will know what to do, are you cer-tain?
MEG
(to Alice)
Tu
You're

M
cor - ri il tuo ri - schio col gros - so com - par.
tak - ing your chanc - es with might - y Sir John.
f
ALI.
(to Quickly)
Se sbagli ti fischio.
. . . and watch his ad- vanc-es!
QUI.
Io sto alla ve - detta.
I'll stay at the cur-tain.
pp
f
pp
f
NAN.
Io resto in di - spar - te sul - l'u - scio a spi - ar.
And I'd bet-ter go, but be sure I'll look on!
pp

ALI.
MODERATO ♩ = 100
E mostreremo al_l'uom che l'al_le_gri_a D'o_neste
Now let us show our hus-bands so im-pe-rious That fun and
(36)
MODERATO ♩ = 100
p
A
donne ogni onestà com_por_ta. Fra le fe_mine quella è la più
fol-ly need not dis-grace a la-dy. When a wom-an pre-tends to be too
f
pp
(darkening her voice)
COME PRIMA
ri_a Che fa la gatta_mor_ta.
NAN. se-rious She's like-ly to be shad-y!
Gaie co_mari di
Mer-ri-ly pull-ing the
MEG
Gaie co_mari di
Mer-ri-ly pull-ing the
COME PRIMA
f
m.d.
p e stacc.

(Quickly goes to the window at the rear, watching the street.)
A
N
M
Ga - - - - - ie co -
Ah, yes, we'll
Vind - sor, ga - ie co - ma - ri di Vind - sor, è
cur - tain, Mer - ri - ly pull - ing the cur - tain, We'll
Vind - sor, ga - ie co - ma - ri di Vind - sor, è
cur - tain, Mer - ri - ly pull - ing the cur - tain, We'll
- ma - ri, è l'o - ra d'al - zar la ri - sa - ta so - no - ra, è l'o - ra d'al -
meet him in style And will greet with a smile And en - treat and be - guile, And then
l'o - ra, è l'o - ra d'al - zar la ri - sa - ta so - no - ra, è l'o - ra d'al -
meet him in style And will greet with a smile And en - treat and be - guile, And then
l'o - ra, è l'o - ra d'al - zar la ri - sa - ta so - no - ra, è l'o - ra d'al -
meet him in style And will greet with a smile And en - treat and be - guile, And then
mf
molto stacc. sempre e cres.

A
-zar la ri-sa-ta so - no-ra, so-no-ra, so-no-ra!
beat and re-vile, And de - feat and de-file him with laughter!
N
-zar la ri-sa-ta so - no-ra, so-no-ra, so-no-ra!
beat and re-vile, And de - feat and de-file him with laughter!
M
-zar la ri-sa-ta so - no-ra, so-no-ra, so-no-ra!
beat and re-vile, And de - feat and de-file him with laughter!
(37)
p
A
Do-v'è?
But where?
N
Presto.
Hur-ry!
M
(rejoining the others)
QUI.
Eccolo! È lui! Poco di-scosto.
Qui-et now! He's here. Right near the en-trance.
p
p

(to Ann, directing her to the exit at the left)
(to Meg, motioning her to leave to the right)
A
Tu di qua. Tu di là. Al posto!
You go there! And you there! Your plac-es!
(running off to the left)
N
Al
Let's
M
Q
A sa-lir s'av-vi-a.
He is in the door-way.
(Alice sits down at the table. She takes the lute and plays a few chords.)
A
N
po-sto!
hur-ry!
(running off to the right)
M
Al po-sto!
Our plac-es!
(running off towards the rear)
Q
Al po-sto!
Let's hur-ry!

(38) MODERATO ♩. = 60
(Guitar)
f
(entering rapidly. Seeing her play the lute, he starts singing:)
FALSTAFF
leggero
Al - fin t'ho
"I broke you,
FAL
allarg.
dolce
col - to raggian - te fior....... T'ho col - - to!...
blos - som so fair, so dear, I broke you!"

(He tries to embrace Alice who stops playing and rises.)
ALL° MOD.to ♩ = 88
L
Ed or po_trò mo_rir fe _ li _ ce. A_vrò vis_su_to
Come, King of Death, I now ig - nore you: For par- a -dise has
(39)
ALL° MOD.to ♩ = 88
p
L
mol _ to do _ po que _ st'o_ra di be _ a _ to a_
o - pened in the en - chant-ment of su - preme de -
ALI.
O so_a_ve Sir John!
Oh, my charm-ing Sir John!
L
_mor. Mia bella A _ li _ _ ce!
-light! How I a dore - - you!
3 3
pp

FAL
Non so far lo sve_ne_vole, Nè lu_sin_
I am not made for jol-li-ty, I can-not
FAL
_gar, nè u_sar frase fio_ri_ta, Ma di_rò
spin such fine, flow-er-y phras-es. But I'll re-
ALI.
Cio_è?
How so?
FAL
tosto un mio pen_sier col_pe_vo_le. Cio_
-veal to you an odd fri-vol-i-ty: I

_è: Vor _ rei che Ma _ stro Ford passas _ se a miglior
wish . . . I wish that Mas - ter Ford should rest be - neath the
pp
ALI.
Perchè?
And why?
vi _ ta... Perchè? - Lo chiedi? Saresti la mia La _ dy e Falstaff il tuo
dai-sies! And why? You ask me? Then you could be my la - dy, and I could be your
f
Po _ ve _ ra La _ dy in _ ver!
I am too plain, I fear!
Lord! De _ gna d'un Re. T'im _
lord. Fit for a king! My

LO STESSO TEMPO ♩ = 88
sostenuto
FAL
-ma_gi_no fre - giata del mio stem - - - ma,
(40) coat of arms, en- - no-bled by your beau - - - ty,
LO STESSO TEMPO ♩ = 88
p
p
FAL
Mo_strar fra gemma e gemma la pompa del tuo sen... Nel -
Will shine a-new when worn by you on your heav-ing heart! Your
ALLEGRETTO ♩ = 88 Lo stesso movimento
FAL
_l'iri ar_den_te e mobi_le dei rai del_l'ada_man_te, Col
eyes will steal the milk-y glow Of pearls crav-ing to grace you, Your
ALLEGRETTO ♩ = 88 Lo stesso movimento
pp
FAL
picciol piè nel no_bi_le cer_chio d'un guardin_fan_te Ri -
bos-om feel the silk-y flow Of gowns ea-ger to en-lace you. The
f

L
-splende-rai più fulgi-da d'un am - pio arco-ba-len.
stars on high will not de-ny Your throne — up in the sky!
(41)
ff
p
ALI.
dolciss. con grazia
O-gni più bel gio - iel mi nuo - ce e spregio il fin-to
In all this splen-dor you might scorn me, A wom-an much too
i-do-lo d'or. Mi basta un vel le - ga-to in cro - ce,........
humble for you. Oh let-your-ten-der-ness a - dorn me!
.... un fregio al cin - to e in te-sta un
In-stead of fur-be-lows a rose will
(puts a flower into her hair.)

SEMPRE LO STESSO MOV.to ♩ = 88

(*taking a step away from him*)

A: fior. A_dula _ tor!
do. Oh, please, Sir John!

FAL. (*trying to embrace her*) Si_re _ na! So_li noi siamo e non temiamo ag_
En_chant - ress! You are with me, and no - one will sur-

SEMPRE LO STESSO MOV.to ♩ = 88

p

(*keeping her distance from him*)

A: Ebben? Voi sie _ te nel pec _
You mean . . .? Your con-science will de -

FAL: _gua _ to. Io t'a _ mo!
-prise - you. I love you!

string. a poco a poco

A: _ca _ to!
-spise you.

(*following her*)

FAL: Sempre l'a _ mor l'oc_ca_sï _ o _ ne az_
My con- -science tells me of our hearts' at-

Sir John!..
Sir John!
L
_zec_ca. Chi se_gue vo_ca_zion non
-trac-tion, com-pels me to pur-sue my
cres.
L
pec_ca. T'a - - mo! e non è mia
ac-tion! Pas - - sion nev-er needs ex-
f
ALI. (cutting him short)
Se tan_ta a_ve _ te vul_ ne - ra - bil
not e - ven when it prompts se - vere a -
L
col_pa...
-cus-es . .
(42)
dim.

ALLº. CON BRIO ♩ = 112
A
pol-pa.
-bus-es?
leggeriss.
FAL
Quand'e-ro pag-gio del Du-ca di Nor-folk e-ro sot-
Once when in Nor-folk in serv-ice to the Duke— I was a
ALLº. CON BRIO ♩ = 112
ppp
FAL
-ti-le, sot-ti-le, sot-ti-le, E-ro un mi-raggio va-go, leg-
page then, vi-va-cious and ten-der, I was a swain as light as the
FAL
-gie-ro, gen-ti-le, gen-ti-le, gen-ti-le. Quel-lo e-ra il
rain,—I—was slight then and slen-der, so slen-der! May of my
FAL
tempo del mio verde a-pri-le, Quello era il tempo del mio lie-to
youth, so full of love and rap-ture, Day that in truth I wish I could re-
p

Maggio. Tan_t'e_ra smilzo, flessi _ bi_le e snello Che sa_rei guiz _
- cap-ture! I was as swift and as slick as a spar-row, Nim-ble as a
_ za_to attra_ver_so un a _ nel _ lo. Quand'e_ro paggio e _ ro sot _
deer and as quick as an ar - row. Yes, as a page so youth-ful and
_ ti _ le, e _ ro sot _ ti - - - le, E _ ro un mi _
ten - der, youth-ful and ten - - - - der, I was a
_ raggio va_go, leg _ gie _ ro, gen_ti _ le, gen ti _ le, gen _
swain as light as the rain, I was slight then and slen-der, so
p

ALI.
LO STESSO MOVIMENTO ♩. = 112
Voi mi ce - lia - te.
You real - ly charm me!
FAL
- ti - le!
slen-der!
(43)
LO STESSO MOVIMENTO ♩. = 112
A
Io te - - - mo i vo - stri in - ganni.
And yet I know you'll harm me.
A
Te - mo che a - mia - te...
I have a ri - val!
Meg...
Meg...
FAL.
Chi?
Whom?
Co - lei?........
Good Grace!

Non tra_
Do not
M'è in ug_gia la........ sua fac_cia.
That old, re-pul- -sive crea-ture?
pp
_di_ _te_mi John...
leave me, my John!
Mi par mil_
In-sane with
mf
p
_le an_ _ni d'a_ver_ti fra le brac_
long_ _ing, I love your ev-ery fea_
f

ALI.
(defending herself)
Per cari - tà!...
Please let me go!
QUI.
(from offstage, screaming)
Si-gno-ra A-
Oh, Mis-tress
(He pursues her again, trying to em-brace her.)
(putting his arms around her waist)
FAL
-cia.
-ture.
T'a-mo...
Al-ways . . .
Vie-ni!
Al-ways!
A
Che c'è?
What now?
(out of breath, stammering)
(entering, feigning excitement)
Q
-li - ce!
A - lice!
Signo-ra A-li - ce!
Oh, Mis-tress A - lice!
Mia si-
Please for-
(releasing Alice, confused)
F
Chi va là?
Who is that?

ALLº. AGITATO ♩ = 112
gnora! C'è Mistress Meg, e vuol par_larvi,
give me! 'Tis Mis-tress Meg. She wants to see you . . .
ALLº. AGITATO ♩ = 112
(44)
pp e molto stacc.
sbuffa, strepita, s'abba_ruffa...
trem-bling, stag-ger-ing, and rat-tled.
E vuol pas_
She's at the
FAL.
Al_la ma_lo_ra!
Speak of the Dev-il!
sar e la trat_ten_go a stento...
door. I could not bar her en-try.
ALICE
The
L
Dove m'a_scondo?
Where can I hide?
sempre staccatissimo

ALI.
(Falstaff hides behind the screen. As
Die-tro il pa - ra - ven - to.
screen here will con - ceal you.
MEG
soon as he is out of sight, Quickly motions Meg to enter. Meg enters, pretending to
A -
Oh,
be highly agitated. Quickly turns to leave again.)
M
- li - - ce! Che spa - ven - to! Che
dear me! What an up - - roar! What
(45)
f
M
chias-so! Che di - scordia! Non per - de - re un mo -
tur-moil! What com - mo-tion! A - way from here and

ALI.
Mi - se - ri - cor - dia! Che av -
My Good-ness - cious! What
8va
men - to, fug - gi!...
quick - ly! Hur - ry!
pp c sempre stacc.
- ven - ne?
hap - pened?
Il tuo con - sor - te vien gri - dan - do ac - cor -
Your hus - band's voice shakes ev - ery roof - top and
(under her breath)
3
(Par - la più for - te.)
(Can you speak loud - er?)
- r'uo - mo! Di - ce... Che
gird - er, Howl - ing. . . . . . that
p

A
M
(Non ri-de-re.)
(Con - tain your-self!)
(almost bursting out with laughter)
vuol scan - na - re un uo-mo!
he is bent on mur-der.
M
Ei cor - re - va in - va - so da tre - men - do fu -
He is on his way, in - sane and fran - tic with
M
- ror! Ma-le-di - cen - do tut - te le fi - glie
rage, And e-ven curs - - es wom-en in bit - ter
f

ALI.
Mi-se-ri-cor - - - dia!
My Good-ness gra - - - cious!
d'E - va!
fu - ry.
(46)
ff
pp
ff
Di - ce che un tuo gan - zo hai na - sco-sto, Lo
Sure that you're con - ceal - ing a lov - er He
p
vuo-le ad o-gni co - - - sto sco - prir...
prom-is - es to skin him a - live.
QUIC.
(returning in great agitation, screaming more loudly than before)
Si - gno-ra A -
May Heav-en
ff tutta forza

Q
li - ce! Vien mastro Ford! Sal - va-te-vi! È
help us! 'Tis Mas-ter Ford! Go, hide your-self! He'll
co - me u - na tem - pe - sta! Strepi - ta, tuo - na,
tear us all a - sun - der. Deaf-en-ing, roar - ing,
ff
ful-mi-na, Si dà dei pu-gni in te - sta, Scop - -
shat-ter-ing, He's roll - ing in like thun - der, Vi - -
ff
ALI.
(somewhat alarmed, under her breath to Quickly)
(Das - sen - no op - pur da
(In jest or are you
- pia in minac - cie ed ur - la...
- o - lent and de - lir - ious.
(47) ff p dim.

PIÙ MOSSO ♩= 138
bur_la?)
se-rious?)
Das_sen_no.
I'm se-rious.
E_gli sca_val _ ca le
In wild vex- a - tion, A
PIÙ MOSSO ♩= 138
pp
f
pp staccatissimo
sie_pi del giar_di_no... Lo se_gue u_na gran
crowd of peo-ple near him, As red as a car-
cal- -ca di gen_te... è già vi_ci_no...
-na- -tion. He's run-ning . . . I seem to hear him!

Q
Men_tr'io vi par - lo ei val - ca l'in-
Oh think of your sal - va - tion I
FOR.
(screaming from offstage) f
Ma_lan-
I will
p
Q
-gres_so...
pray you . . .
FOR
-dri - no!!
spear him!
(He already has set out to flee but stays when hearing Ford's voice. Alice folds the screen around him to conceal him completely.)
FAL.
Il dia_vo_lo ca _ val - ca sul - l'ar_co d'un vio_
Those fid-dles spell dam - na - tion and give me cause to
(from upstage, shouting to those who follow him)
FOR
Chiu_de_te le
Now block all the
FAL
_li - no!!
fear him!
(48) ppp

(After Ford, enter Dr. Cajus and Fenton.)
FOR
por-te! Sbarra-te le sca-le! Segui-temi a cac-cia! Scoviamo il ci-
door-ways and watch in the al-ley! We'll see the se - duc - er in chains on a
(to Cajus)
-gna-le! Cor-re-te sul-l'or-me, sul-l'u-sta.
gal - ley! You fol-low his scent till you find him!
(to Bardolph and Pistol, pointing to the right)
(to Fenton)
Tu fru-ga ne-gli an-di-ti. Sven-ta - te la
BAR.
Ex-plore all the pas-sag-es! Cut off his es-
A cac-cia!
To ac-tion!
(storming into the room, shouting, while Fenton runs to the left)
PIS.
A cac-cia!
To ac-tion!

ALICE
(somewhat haughtily, to Ford)
Sei tu dis-sen-na-to? Che
You seem to be cra-zy... but
(Bardolph and Pistol run into the adjoining room.)
FOR
fu-ga! Cer-ca-te là den-tro!
-cape and ex-amine the pan-try!
p
A
fai? (noticing the basket)
why?
FOR
Chi c'è den-tro quel
Well, well... what's in the
(49)
A
Il bu-ca-to.
Dirt-y lin-en.
FOR
ce-sto?
bas-ket?

(to Alice)
FORD
Mi la - - vi!! rea
Yes, dirt - - y, quite
mo - glie!
dirt - y!
(to Cajus, handing him a bunch of keys)
Tu, pi-glia le
Go, here are the
chia-vi, ro-vi-sta le cas-se!
keys to the cup-boards and cas-kets.
(to Alice)
Ben tu mi la - vi!
An - - gel of vir - tue!

(kicking the basket)
(shouting towards the rear)
FOR
Al dia-vo-lo i cen-ci! Spran-ga - te - mi
To hell with these tat-ters! Go on, rec - on-
f
(starts pulling the wash out of the basket, strewing it all over the floor)
l'u - scio del par-co! Ca-
-noi - ter the gar-den! The
50
p
-mi - cie... gon-nel - le... Or ti
draw-ers... and blous-es... now I'll
sgu - scio bric-con! Strofi-
catch you, you lout! ...dirt-y

(searching furiously)
-nacci! Via!.. Via!.. Cuffie rotte! -Ti
nap-kins, out! Out! Here some stock-ings! I'll
sguscio- Len-zuo-la... berretti da not-te...
catch you . . . and bed-sheets... some sil-ly old night-caps...
(51)
pp
f
Facilitato
(looking at the scattered wash)
ALI.
Che u-ra-ga-no!!
Howl-ing tem-pest!
MEG
Che u-ra-ga-no!!
Howl-ing tem-pest!
QUIC.
Che u-ra-ga-no!!
Howl-ing tem-pest!
-Non c'è... Cer-
... not yet! Go,

FOR
-chiam sot - to il let - to, Nel for - no, nel
search in the at - tic, the cis - tern, the
p
(running to and fro, yelling to all and sundry)
FOR
poz - zo, nel ba - gno, sul tet - to, In can-
ar - bor, The kit - chen, the bed - room and the
cres.
ALI.
È far - netico! Troviamo
He's a lu-na-tic! How can our
QUIC.
Cogliam tempo.
Let us hur-ry!
(off to the left)
FOR
-ti - na...
cel - lar!
(52)
f
pp

mo - do co - m'e - gli e - sca.
MEG. port - ly friend es - cape him?
No,
No,
Nel pa - nier.
In the bas - ket!
là dentro non c'en - tra, è trop - - po
it nev - er will hold him. He's far too
FAL. (shaken up, has cautiously opened the screen)
gros - so.
bulk - y. (running to the basket)
Ve - diam;
Let's see!

(trying to squeeze into the basket)
FAL
sì
Ah . . .
c'en - tro,
it is . . .
ALI.
(exits to the rear)
Cor - ro a chiama - re i ser - vi.
I'll go to call the serv - ants.
(to Falstaff, feigning surprise)
MEG
Sir
Sir
FAL
c'en - tro.
eas - y . . .
(53)
M
John! Voi qui? Voi?
John, you here . . . you?
(still fighting the basket)
FAL
T'a - mo!
An - gel!

L
A - mo te so - la...
On - ly be - lov - ed!
sal - vami!
Help me now!
MEG
Le - sto!
Head down!
QUIC.
(to Falstaff, collecting the pieces of wash)
Svel - to!
Hur - ry!
L
sal - va-mi!
Res - cue me!
Svel - to!
Head down!

MEG
Svel - to!
Hur - ry!
(making a supreme effort to squeeze fully into the basket)
FAL
Ahi! Ahi!
Ah, ouch!
cres.
FAL
Ci sto... Co - pri te mi...
I'm in. Now cov-er me!
(Ann and Fenton enter from the left, speaking softly and cautiously.)
NAN.
(Vien
Come
QUIC.
Pre - sto! colmiamo il ce - sto.
Grum-ble be-fore you tum-ble!
f

ALL.º ♩= 138 LO STESSO MOV.to
(moving toward the screen)
(Fenton follows her.)
qua.
here!
Quanti schia_mazzi!
Don't be so la-zy!
Segui il mio
Come, let us
FENTON
Che chiasso!
I wor-ry!
ALL.º ♩= 138 LO STESSO MOV.to
(54)
p
passo.
hur-ry!
Qui ognun de _ li _ ra
See how they're fum-ing,
Ca_sa di pazzi!
All this is cra-zy!
con vario er_ror. Son paz _ zi d'i _ ra...
jos-tle and shove, As mad with fu - ry...
E noi d'a_mor.
...as we with love!

(taking him by the hand to pull him behind the screen)
N
Seguimi. A-dagio. Toc-
Fol-low me, but light-ly! The
FEN
Nes-sun m'ha scorto.
I'm here be-side you.
pp
N
-chia-mo il por-to. Sta
screen will hide you... We're
FEN
Sia-mo a no-str'a-gio.
shield-ing us tight-ly.
N
zit-to e at-ten-to.
safe from de-tec-tion.
(drawing her close)
FEN
Vien sul mio pet-to!
Let me ca-ress-you!
cres.

Il pa-ra-ven-to sia be-ne-det-to!
Wel-come pro-tec-tion, Fond-ly we bless you!
sia be-ne-det-to!
Fond-ly we bless you!
Dr. CAJUS
(yelling from outside)
Al
Be-
p
Io TEMPO ♩= 138
(enters, running across the room)
la-dro!
-head him!
Squar-tate-lo!
and quar-ter him!
FORD
(yelling from outside)
(running in, while Bardolph and Pistol come in from the right)
(55)
Al pa-gliar-do! Al la-dro!
To the gal-lows! The scoun-drel!
Io TEMPO ♩= 138
ff
BARDOLFO
(to Pistol)
(to Bardolph)
Non c'è, no.
Not here! No.
C'è? C'è?
There? There?
PISTOLA
No.
No.
mf

Dr. C
(searching in the fire-place and looking up the chimney)
Non
Where
(running about, searching the chest)
FOR
Va - da a soq-qua - dro la ca - sa.
I vow to Sa - tan I'll find him!
poco cres.
Dr. C
tro - vo nes - su - no.
is he, I won - der.
(Pistol and Bardolph exit to the left.)
FOR
Eppur giu-ro, che l'uomo è qua
I swear he still is here in the
(56)
p
Dr. C
Sir John!............ Sa-rò
Sir John, I'll be
FOR
dentro. Ne so-no si - cu-ro, si - cu-ro, si - cu-ro!
house. Yes, I know it for cer-tain, I know it for cer-tain.

ga - io quel dì che ti ve - da dar cal - ci a ro - va - io!
dy - ing with laugh - ter The day you will hang from the raft - er.
(trying to break open the cupboard)
FOR.
Vien fuo - ra, fur - fan - te! O bom - bar - do le
Come out here, you ron - yon, or I'll tear you to
poco sensibile
Dr. C.
(looking for a key to the cupboard)
T'ar - ren - di!
Sur - ren - der!
mu - ra! Vien fuo - ra! Co -
tat - ters! Come out here, you
p

BAR.
(re-entering from the left)
Nes - su - no!
There's no - one!
(still busy, with
FOR
-dar - do! Su - gliar - do! Cer-ca-te-lo an-
trai - tor! You cow - ard! You filth-y rap-
PIS.
Nes - su - no!
There's no one!
cres.
Dr. Cajus, trying to open the cupboard while Bardolph and Pistol re-exit to where they came
FOR
-co - ra! T'ar-ren - di! Scan-
-scal - lion! Sur-ren - der, you
from)
(finally opening the cupboard)
FOR
-far-do! Non c'è!!
de - mon! Not here?
(57)
pp

Dr. C.
(opening the chest)
Vien fuo - ra!
Sur - ren - der!
Non
Not
C
(runs through the room, searching)
c' è !!
here?
Pappa_lar - do! Be_òn!
You de-bauch - er, you'll wish
Bada a
you were
C
te!...........................
dead!
(opening the drawer of the little table)
Sca_gnar_do!
You lech - er,
Fal_sar_do!
you vil - lain!
FOR.
Sca_gnar - do! Fal_sar - do! Sca - gnar_do! Bric -
You Sa - tan, you lech - er, you vil - lain, you
(58)
ff
tr

(During all this, Ann and
Dr. C
Sca - gnar-do! Fal-sar-do! Bric - con!
You lech-er-ous vil-lain, come out!
F
- con!
lout!
Sca - gnar-do! Fal-sar-do! Bric - con!
You lech-er-ous vil-lain, come out!
ff
Fenton have paid no heed to the turmoil around them. Their caresses come to a head in a resounding kiss which immediately stops all activity. Everyone has heard the sound of the kiss.)
NAN.
bacio
FEN.
bacio
Dr. C
C'è.
There!
(whispering, his eyes on the screen)
FOR
C'è.
There!
mf
pp
sempre a tempo
ANDANTE ♩ = 80
(cautiously approaching the screen)
vuota vuota
Dr. C
Se ti piglio!
When I snatch you . . .
vuota vuota
(cautiously approaching the screen)
FOR
Se t'ag - guanto!
When I catch you . . .
Se t'ac-
When I
ANDANTE ♩ = 80
vuota vuota
(59) p

D.r C
Se t'ac - cef - fo!
When I nab you . . .
FOR
- ciuf - fo!
grab you . . .
Ti scon -
I will
D.r C
T'arronciglio come un can!
I will break your ev-ery bone . . .
Guai a
. . . with a
FOR
- quasso!
thrash you . . .
Ti rompo il cef - fo!
. . . beat up and smash you.
f
QUIC.
(near the basket, to Meg)
Fac - cia - mo le vi - ste d'atten - de - re ai
Our friend in the bas-ket, You can-not de -
(softly)
D.r C
te!
stone!
Guai a
I a -
FOR
Pre - ga il tuo
No - one can
San - to!
save you.
P e stacc.

Q
pan - ni; Pur ch'ei non c'in - gan - ni con mos - se im - pre -
- ny it, Un - less he is qui - et, Turns bas - ket to
D.C
te! Guai!
-lone I
FOR
MEG. (near the basket, to Quickly)
Fac - cia - mo - gli sie - pe fra tan - to scom -
Our cun - ning de - vic - es At first lead to
Q
- vi - ste.
cas - ket.
D.C
cupo
FOR
Guai se al - fin con te m'az -
Wait, you lout, un - til I

-pi - glio. Ne' giuo-chi il pe - ri - glio è un gra - no di
sham - bles, Pro - vid - ing our gam - bles With sa - vor and
Guai!
I
zuf - fo!
clutch you!
Se ti
I shall
pp
ppp
pe - pe.
spic - es.
Fi - n'or non s'ac - cor - se di nul - la, e - gli
He wants to dis - arm us But prog - ress is
Se t'ag -
When I
pi - glio!
kill you!

M
Q
può........ Sor-pren-der-ci for-se, con-fon-der-ci
slow. He still can a-larm us, But harm us, oh
Dr. C
-guan-to!
catch you . . .
FOR
Se t'ac-
I shall
M
Il ri-schio è un di-let-to che ac-cre-sce l'ar-
We're tak-ing our chanc-es As nev-er be-
Q
no.
no!
E-gli
It is
Dr. C
Se t'ac-
When I
FOR
-cef-fo!
kill you!

M
-dor, Che sti-mo-la in pet-to gli spi-ri-ti e il
-fore, But dan-ger en-hanc-es Our fun e-ven
Q
può sor-pren-der-ci for-se, con-fon-der-ci
so. He still may a-larm us, But harm us, oh
C
-ciuf-fo!
snatch you . . .
(entering from the left)
BAR.
Non si tro-va.
PIS (returning with several neighbors) It is use-less.
Non si
We can't
M
cor.
more.
Q
no.
no!
FOR.
(to Bardolph, Pistol, and the others)
Psss...
Pssst . . .
Qua tutti.
be qui-et!
P
coglie.
find him!
(60)
p

(pointing to the screen)
FOR
L' ho trovato.
I have found him.
Là c'è Fal_staff con mia
With my wife he's there in
p
Dr. C.
Zit_to!
Si - lence!
BAR.
Soz_zo can vi_tu_pe_ra_to!
What a scan-dal, what an out-rage!
FOR
mo_glie.
hid - ing.
Zit_to!
Si - lence!
Ur_le_rai
You hold your
PIS.
Zit_to!
Si - lence!
f

QUIC.
(pushing him down)
Sta sot - to, sta
Lie low and keep
(poking his head out of the basket)
FAL.
Af - fo - - go!
I'm chok- - ing.
Dr. C
Zit - to! Zit - to!
Si - lence! Si - lence!
do - po.
thun - der!
zit - to!
Si-lence!
MEG
Or que - sti s'in -
'Tis good for your
sot - to!
qui - et!
Af - fo - - - go!
I'm smok- - - ing.
Zit - to, zit - to!
BAR.
Not a whis-per!
Zit - to, zit - to!
Not a whis - per!
Là s'è u - di - to il suon d'un
We have heard the sound of

M
-sor - ge.
di - et.
(bending down and addressing Falstaff in the basket)
Q
Se l'al - tro ti scor - ge sei mor - to.
You're caus - ing a ri - ot, be qui - et!
(in the basket)
FAL
Son
I'm
B
Noi dobbiam piglia - re il
In this case of sin - ful
FOR
ba - cio.
kiss - es.
p
M
Sta sot - to, sta sot - to!
Lie low and keep qui - et!
Q
Sta sot - to, sta
You're caus - ing a
FAL
cot - to!
fry - ing!
B
to - po Men - tre sta roden - do
bliss - es Slay the man and spare the

FEN.
Cantabile
(to Ann)
Bel_la! ri_
So sweet and
O
sot_to.
ri - ot!
B
ca_cio.
mis-sus!
FOR.
Ra_gioniam.
Not so fast!
(61)
pp
NAN.
(to Fenton)
leggiero
Men_tre quei vec_chi cor_ron la
They yell and chat_ter Hunt_ing their
FEN
_den - te!
ten - der
Oh! co - me
I feel you
FOR
Col - po non
Now pay at -

N
gio - stra Noi di sot - tec - chi cor - riam la
quar - ry. What does it mat - ter, We shall not
FEN
pie - - ghi ver - so i miei
MEG. near me, For - ev - er
QUIC.
FAL.
Dr. C
BAR.
FOR
vi - bro sen - z'un pia - - no di bat -
PIS. -ten - tion! We shall draw a plan of
TENORS
NEIGHBORS
BASSES

no - stra. L'a - mor non o - de tuon nè bu -
wor - ry. Thun - der and light - ning To us are not
prie - ghi don - ne - sca -
cheer me Your ra - diant
Un uom di quel ca -
A man of vast di -
Bra - vo!
Splen-did!
- ta - glia.
bat - tle.
Bra - vo!
Splen-did!
Bra - vo!
Splen-did!
Bra - vo!
Splen-did!

N
_fe _ re,
fright - 'ning.
Vola alle sfe - - - - re be - -
On-ward I fly, a dove On-
FEN
_men _ te!
splen - dor!
Co _ me ti vi _ di m'innamo_
I stood be - fore you, Un-der your
M
Q
FAL
Dr. C
li _ bro con un soffio ci sba _ ra _ glia!
-men- sion, He may slaugh-ter us like cat - tle.
B
FOR
La mia tatti _ ca ma_e - - - -
I'm a mas-ter at de-cep - - - -
P

N
FEN
M
Q
FAL
Dr C
B
FOR
P
dolciss.
-a- - -te e go- - - - - - -
gold- - - -en wings of
-rai, E tu sor - ri - di per-chè lo
spell, How I a - dore - you, You know it
-stra le sue mos-se pria re-gi- - - - - - -
-tion, Let me tell you my con-cep- - - - - - -

N
- de.
love.
FEN
sai.
well!
M
Q
FAL
Dr. C
B
(to Pistol and two neighbors)
più marcato
(to Bardolph and Dr. Cajus)
FOR
- stra. Voi sa - re - te l'a - la de - stra. Noi sa - rem l'a - la si -
- tion: While the right wing will dis - lodge him On the left we'll draw and
P
(62)

Già un so - gno bel - lo d'I - me - ne al - -
The God of Love has for - ev - er
(to everyone else)
- ni - stra, E co - stor con piè ga - gliar - do sfon - de - ran - no il ba - lu -
dodge him. Then the cen - ter un - der cov - er Will ex - ter - min - ate our

N
Lo spi - ri - tel - lo d'a-mor, vol -
The stars a - bove web a veil a -
FEN
- beg - gia, un so - gno
bound us, The God of
M
Q
FAL
Dr C
A - spettiam un tuo se -
Tell us when and we'll be
B
Bra - vo, bra - vo ge - ne - ra - le!
What a fine dis - play of cun - ning!
FOR
- ar - do.
lov - er.
P
Bra - vo, bra - vo ge - ne - ra - le!
What a fine dis - play of cun - ning!
Bra - vo, bra - vo ge - ne - ra - le!
What a fine dis - play of cun - ning!
Bra - vo, bra - vo ge - ne - ra - le!
What a fine dis - play of cun - ning!
mf

teg - gia, lo spi - ri - tel - lo d'a - mor, vol -
-round - us, The stars a - bove web a veil a -
bel - lo d'I - me - ne al -
Love has for - ev - er
Sta sot - to!
Be qui - et!
(poking his head out of the basket)
Sta
Be
Che cal - do! Mi squa - glio!
I'm fry - ing! I'm dy - ing!
-gna - le.
run-ning.
Bra - vo, bra - vo!
Tru - ly stun - ning!
Bra - vo, bra - vo!
Tru - ly stun - ning!
Bra - vo, bra - vo!
Tru - ly stun - ning!
Bra - vo, bra - vo!
Tru - ly stun - ning!

N
- teg - gia.
- round us.
FEN
- beg - gia.
bound us.
M
Il ri - bal - do vor - reb - be un ven -
How much more can we do for his
Q
sot - to!
qui - et!
FAL
Dr. C
Bra - vo, bra - vo!
Tru - ly stun - ning!
B
Bra - vo, bra - vo!
Tru - ly stun - ning!
FOR
P
Bra - vo, bra - vo!
Tru - ly stun - ning!
Bra - vo, bra - vo!
Tru - ly stun - ning!
Bra - vo, bra - vo!
Tru - ly stun - ning!

N
EN
M
- taglio.
com-fort?
Q
Ti metto il ba-vaglio se par -
You're court-ing your death, so be si -
(pleading, his nose still visible)
AL
Un breve spiraglio non chiedo di più.
Just one sin-gle breath or in clothes I will drown!
C
B
OR
P
mf

p espressivo
N
Tut - - to de - -
Try - - ing to
FEN
(pushing Falstaff down beneath the laundry)
Fra quei - - - le
Your eyes shall
M
Giù! giù! giù!
Down! Down! Down!
Q
-li. Giù! giù! giù!
-lent! Down! Down! Down!
FAL
(to Ford, holding an ear to the screen)
p
Dr. C
Sento,
Yes, I
B
(to Dr. Cajus, holding an ear to the screen)
p
FOR
Senti, accosta un po' l'orecchio!
Bend an ear and you can hear them!
P
p
Ma fra poco il lieto
If he knew that we are
pppp
S'e - - - gli
Sin - - - ful
S'e - - - gli
Sin - - - ful
(63)
mf p mf
p cantabile con espress.
pp stacc.

li - - - ra,
flee you,
N
ci - - - glia
meet me,
Par - liam sot - to - vo - ce guar - dan - do il Mes -
We bet - ter de - fy him And bet - ter be -
Co - stui s'è in - far - da - to di tan - ta vil -
'Tis real - ly a quan - dary: So black is our
L
C
sen - to,
hear them,
È la vo - ce
I am cer - tain
R
giuo - co
near him!
ca - - de più non
love may bring you
ca - - de più non
love may bring you

N
so - - spi - - - ro e
Sigh - - ing, de - - - -
FEN
veg - go due
Ra - diant, be - - -
M
-ser
-ware.
Q
-tà
swain,
FAL
Dr. C
sen-to, in
I per-
B
FOR
Che pa-te-ti-ci la-men-ti!!
Hear their bill-ing and their coo-ing!
P
tur-be-rà du-ra le-
He would quick-ly change his
scap - - pa, nes - sun
glo - - ry While the
scap - - pa, nes - sun
glo - - ry While the

ri - - - - so
-lir - - - - - ious,
fa - - - - ri
-guil - - - - - ing,
Che bron - to - la e cuo - ce nel no - stro pa -
'Tis bet - ter to fry him Than ren - der him
Che dar - lo al bu - ca - to è a - ver - ne pie -
That e - ven a laun - dry Won't clean him a -
-ten - do e ve - do
-ceive it But can't be -
del - la don - na
'tis the wom - an
-zion.
tune.
più lo può sal - -
sin - - ning's go - - - ing
più lo può sal - -
sin - - ning's go - - - ing

N
sor - ri - de il vi - - - - - - - -
My heart mys - te - - - - - - - -
FEN
a me ra - vi - - - - - - - -
Like star - lets smil - - - - - - - -
M
- nier, che.......... bron - - - to - la e
rare, 'Tis bet - - - ter to
Q
- tà che dar - - - lo al bu -
- gain, That e - - - ven a
FAL
D.C
chia - ro del - le
- lieve it. Can it
B
FOR
Su quel ni - do d'u - si - gnuo - li.
From this hot - bed of mis - do - ing
P
E - gli can - ta ma fra
In a mo - ment I shall
- var. Nel tuo dia - vo - lo t'in -
well: 'Twill be quite an - oth - er
- var. Nel tuo dia - vo - lo t'in -
well: 'Twill be quite an - oth - er

-so e il cor so - spi - - - - - - - -
-rious Cries out to see
-glia se - re - ni e chia - - - - - - - -
-ing Come down to greet
cuo - - - ce nel no - - - stro pa -
fry him Than ren - - der him
ca - - - to e a - - - ver - - - ne pie -
laun - - - dry Won't clean him a -
fem - mi - ne del - le fem - mi - ne gl'in -
real - ly be . . . Can a wom - an be so
che ri - sponde al ca - va -
An - swer - ing her lov - er's
scop - pie - rà fra po - co il tuon.
I'll dis - patch him to the moon.
po - co mu - te - rà la sua can -
spear him: I should say 'tis none too
cap - pa che tu pos - sa stra - maz -
sto - ry When you pay for it in
cap - pa che tu pos - sa stra - maz -
sto - ry When you pay for it in

N
dolciss.
-ra. Dol - ci richiami d'a - mor.
you. Sweet is the tor-ment of love!
FEN
-ri. Dim - mi se m'a - - me
me. (having returned to the basket) Tell me you love me
ALI.
Silenzio!
Be qui-et!
M
-nier,
rare,
Q
-tà.
-gain.
(huffing and puffing)
FAL
Ouff! Cesto molesto!
Oh, oh, hear me-crying!
D.r C
-ganni.
-bold?
B
-lier.
call.
pp (to the others)
FOR
Zitto! A noi! Quest'è il mo-
Si-lence! Stand by! This is our
P
-zon.
soon.
-zar!
Hell.
-zar!
Hell.
dolciss.

Si........................ t'a - mo t'a - mo! t'a - - - - -
Yes, ____ I shall love you for - ev - er. I love
- mi?
too?
t'a - - - - -
I love
Che bestia restì - a.
Why, how can you dare it?
Che bestia restì - a.
Why, how can you dare it?
(emerging once more)
Protesto!
I'm dy-ing!
- mento.
mo-ment.
Zitto!
Si-lence!
At - tenti!
At - ten-tion!
attenti a
And fol-low
N
L
C
R

N
- mo!
you
t'a
al
FEN
- mo!
you
t'a
al
A
M
È matto fu-ribondo!
He must have lost his senses.
Q
È matto fu-ribondo!
He must have lost his senses.
(screaming)
(hiding)
FAL
Portatemi vi-a!
Ah, I can-not bear it!
A-iuto!
Oh, help me!
aiuto!
Oh, help me!
a-iuto!
Oh, help me!
D.r C
Dà il segnal.
Tell us when!
B
FOR
me.
me!
Uno...
One . . .
Due...
two . . .
P
(64)

ALL.º COME PRIMA ♩ = 138
(With the screen removed, Ann and Fenton are momentarily stunned.)
- mo!
- ways.
- mo!
- ways.
È il fi - ni -
The search has
È il fi - ni -
The search has
È il fi - ni -
The search has
Non è lui!!
Where is he?
(On the count of "Three" the men open the screen, revealing Ann and Fenton in tender embrace. Utmost consternation is on everyone's face.)
Sba - lor - di -
The search has
Tre.
three !
Sba - lor - di -
The search has
Sba - lor - di -
The search has
Sba - lor - di -
The search has
Sba - lor - di -
The search has
ALL.º COME PRIMA ♩ = 138
(65)
ff

f
N
Ah!
f
Ah!
FEN
Ah!
Ah!
A
-mon - - do!
end - - ed!
M
-mon - - do!
end - - ed!
Q
-mon - - do!
end - - ed!
FAL
f
DrC
Ah!
Ah!
B
-men - - to!
end - - ed!
FOR
-men - - to!
end - - ed!
P
-men - - to!
end - - ed!
-men - - to!
end - - ed!
-men - - to!
end - - ed!
ff

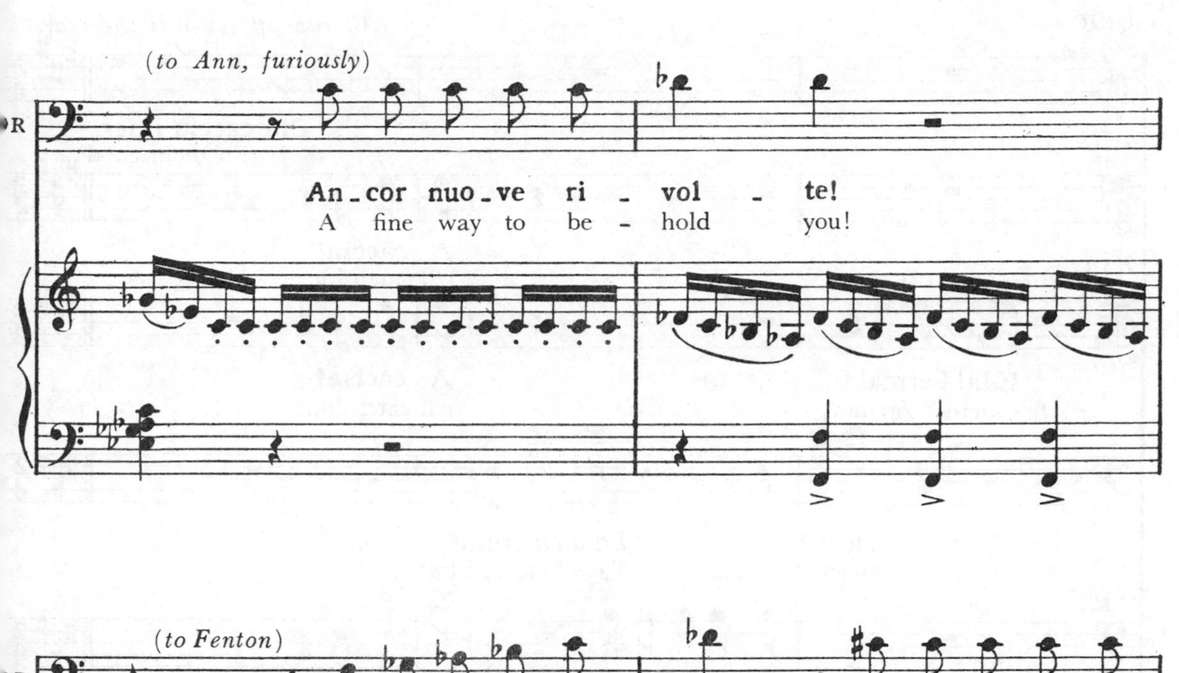
(to Ann, furiously)
R
An_cor nuo_ve ri _ vol _ te!
A fine way to be - hold you!

(to Fenton)
R
Tu va pe' fat_ti tuoi! L'ho det_to mil_le
From now on you'll o - - bey. How of - ten have I
mf

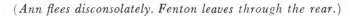

(Ann flees disconsolately. Fenton leaves through the rear.)

R
vol_te: Co_stei non fa per voi.
told you: Keep off my daugh-ter's way!
ff

QUIC.
(All run off towards the rear)
Che caccia infer - - na - le!
I wish them good hunt-ing!
Dr.C.
A caccia!
We'll catch him.
BAR.
(running to the rear)
È là! Ferma!
He's there! Stop him!
A caccia!
We'll catch him.
FOR
Dove?
Where?
Squarta_telo!
Take hold of him!
PIS.
Là! sulle scale.
There, on the staircase!
A caccia!
We'll catch him.
NEIGHBORS
A caccia!
We'll catch him.
A caccia!
We'll catch him.
LO STESSO MOVIMENTO ♩ = 138
Q
LO STESSO MOVIMENTO ♩ = 138
ff
(66)

ALI.
(calling to the rear)
(Ann returns with four servants and a page.)
Ned! Will! Tom! Isä_ac! Su! Pre_sto!
Ned! Will! Tom! And Jack! Come! Come here
pp
A
Pre_sto!
quick-ly!
(67)
Ro_ve_
Go and
f
p
A
_scia _ te quel ce_sto Dal_la fi _ ne _ stra nel_
emp _ ty this bas-ket out of the win _ dow and
3

A
- l'ac - qua del fos-so... Là! presso alle giun - ca - ie Davanti al
in - to the riv - er, there, where you see the wom-en a-bout to
A
croc - chio del - le la - van - da - ie.
NAN.
laun - der all the dirt - y lin - en!
Sì, sì, sì, sì!
Yes, yes, yes, yes!
MEG
Sì, sì, sì, sì!
Yes, yes, yes, yes!
QUIC.
Sì, sì, sì, sì!
Yes, yes, yes, yes!
f
(to the servants trying to lift the basket)
N
C'è dentro un pez - zo
(68)
It may be some-what

ALI.
(to the page who obeys her request)
Tu chia - ma mio ma - ri - to;
You go and call my mas - ter . . .
gros - so.
heav - y.
pp leggerissimo
(to Meg, while Ann and Quickly watch the servants lifting the basket)
Gli nar - re - remo il no - stro ca - so paz - zo.
so he may wit - ness old Sir John's dis - as - ter.
So - lo al ve - der il Ca - va - lier nel
See - ing his ri - val in this sad con -
p

A
guaz - zo
- di - tion
D'o-gni ge - lo-sa ubbì - a sa-rà gua-
Should cool his own sus-pi- - cion That much
f
p
A
- ri - - - to.
fast - - - er.
(69)
ff
(to the servants approaching the window)
A
Co - raggio!
Come on now!
NAN.
Il fondo ha fat-to crac!
The bot-tom will fall out.
MEG
Co - raggio!
Come on now!
QUIC.
(to the servants)
Pe - sa!
Try it!

(The basket is raised.)
A
N
M
Q
Tri - on - fo!
Up - end it!
Che
That's
Su!
Up!
Tri - on - fo!
Up - end it!
Ah! Ah!
Ha, ha!
Su!
Up!
Tri - on - fo!
Up - end it!
Ah! Ah!
Ha, ha!
Su!
Up!
Tri - on - fo!
Up - end it!
Ah! Ah!
Ha, ha!
f
p
p
tonfo!
splen-did!
(Ford and the others come back.)
Che tonfo!
That's splen-did!
Che tonfo!
That's splen-did!
dim.
pp
pp
morendo

ALI., NAN., MEG e QUIC.
(The contents of the basket, including Falstaff, tumble out the window. Alice has taken her husband's arm and led him to the window. Great hilarity all around.)
ff
BAR.
Pata - trac!
What a splash!
ff
FOR. e PIS.
Pata - trac!
What a splash!
ff
TENORS
Pata - trac!
What a splash!
NEIGHBORS
ff
BASSES
Pata - trac!
What a splash!
ff
Pata - trac!
What a splash!
(70)
fff tutta forza
ff sempre
(fast curtain)

Act Three

Part One

NOTHING FOR PISTOL IN PT 1

An open square.

To the right the Garter Inn with the sign inscribed HONY SOIT QUI MAL Y PENSE. Next to the entrance a bench of stone. It is near sunset.

poco cres.
(2)
cres.
cres. sempre
(3)
ff e sempre stacc.

(curtain)
(4) ff
(Falstaff is seated on the bench, deep in thought.)
ppp
p dim.
pp

(Suddenly he shakes himself violently, pounds the bench with his fist and calls for the innkeeper.)

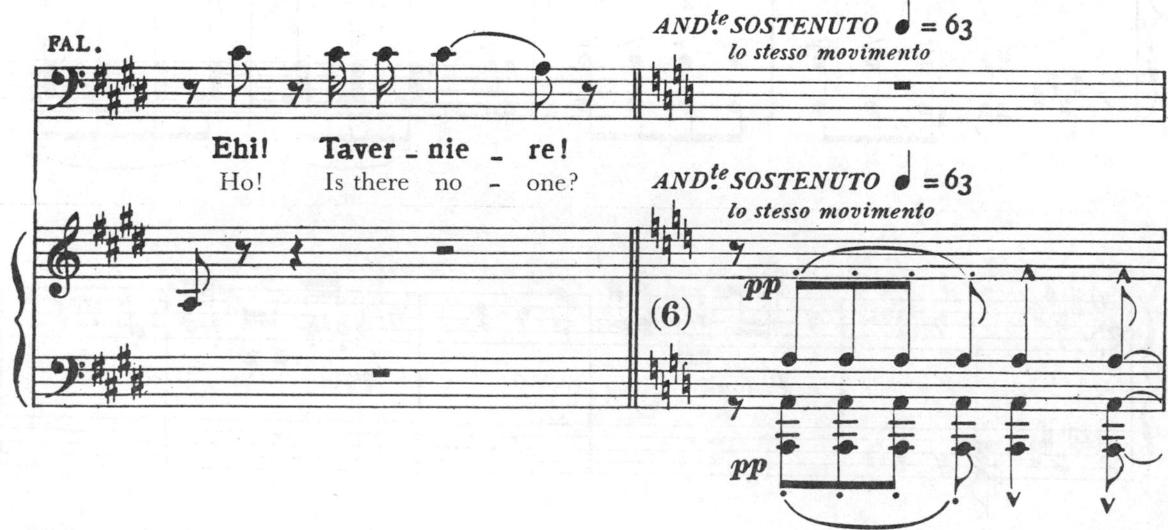

(sinks back into meditation)
Mondo ladro.
Nas-ty world!
Mondo ru_
Vil-lan-ous
_baldo.
world!
(The innkeeper appears.)
Reo mondo!
Vile world!
Taver_niere: un bicchier di vin caldo.
Bring some wine here! Serve it hot to re-vive me!
morendo
ppp
pp
(the innkeeper exits.)
f
Io, dunque, a_vrò vissu_to tan_
John Fal-staff, who led a life of ad-
pp
f
pp

stizzoso
incalz. un poco
FAL
-t'anni, audace e de - stro Cava - lie-re, per es-se-re portato in un ca-
-ven-ture, a no-ble knight,_ a gal-lant fight-er, at last has had to cow-er in a
f
pp
f
p incalz. un poco
FAL
- nestro E gittato al canale coi pannilini biechi, Come si fa coi gatti e i catellini
basket to be dumped in-to a ditch with a load of dirty linen as if he were a cat or some repulsive
p
ALLEGRO 𝅗𝅥 = 63
Lo stesso movimento - tempo doppio
FAL
cie - chi. Che se non ga - leg - gia - - va per
mon-grel! Un - less my might-y paunch like a
ALLEGRO 𝅗𝅥 = 63
Lo stesso movimento - tempo doppio
f
mf

FAL

me que - st'e - pa tron - fia
cork had kept me float - ing

ff

FAL

Cer - to affo - ga vo. -
I should have perished.

f

Brut - ta mor - te. -
filled with wa - ter,

p

FAL

pp

p cres.

L'ac - qua mi gon - - - - -
swell - ing and bloat - - - - -

legato e cres.

pp

tronca

FAL

- - - - fia.
- - - - ing.

COME PRIMA ♩ = 63

COME PRIMA ♩ = 63

Mon - do
Rot - ten

(7)

ppp

FAL
reo._
world!
Non c'è più vir_tù._
All has run to seed.
ppp
ppp
FAL
Tut_to decli_na.
Vir-tue is crum-bling.
COME PRIMA (atto II°) ♩=100
COME PRIMA (atto II°) ♩=100
morendo
p
FAL
Va, vec_chio John, va,
Go, gal-lant John, go,
FAL
va per la tua vi_a; cammi__na fin_chè tu
go on-ward to glo-ry! Go on till you end your

muo - - ia. Al - lor............................ scompa - ri -
jour ney! With you ——— once and for

p

- rà la ve - ra vi - ri - li - tà dal
all will die the en - chant - ed flow'r of

string.

string.

ALL°. COME PRIMA

mondo. _
man-hood.

ALL°. COME PRIMA

(8)

p

p

Che giornatac _ cia nera.
What an in - fer - nal night-mare!

M'a _ iu _ ti il
My gra - cious

p

FAL
ciel!....
Lord!
Impin_guo troppo.
I grow too port-ly,
my
ancora più piano
morendo
(The innkeeper brings a large goblet of hot wine and deposits it on the bench, then exits.)
sottovoce
Ho dei pe _ li gri _ gi........
hair is turn - ing grey
COME PRIMA ♩=126
ff
staccato
cantarellando
Ver _
I
_ sia_mo un po' di vi _ no nel _ l'ac _ qua del Ta _ mi _
trust this brac-ing po - tion will warm the i - cy o -

ALLEGRO ♩ = 100
-gi.
-cean!
(9) ALLEGRO ♩ = 100
mf
(drinks slowly, savoring every sip)
LO STESSO MOVIMENTO ♪ = 100
ppp
FAL.
(unbuttons his vest and stretches comfortably)
Buo - no. -
Splen - did!
Ber del vin
To drink good
ppp
(His mood is changing for the better.)
L
dol - ce e sbotto - nar - - si al so - le;
wine is to en - joy the sun - shine,
dolciss.
pp

♩ = 100 SEMPRE LO STESSO MOV.to

FAL

Dol - - ce co - sa! Il buon
warm and ten - der. All at

vi - no sperde le te - tre fo - le del - lo scon - forto, ac - cende
once, good wine will dis-pel the clouds of sor - row and wor-ry, re-vive the

morendo

p

l'oc - chio e il pen - sier, dal lab - bro sa - le al cer -
heart and the eye. Your mind will flut - ter and

pp

- vel e qui - vi ri - sveglia il picciol fab - bro dei trilli; un negro
fly while mil - lions of bells will ring in joy - ous car- il-lon . . . And sly-ly

parlando

(10)

pp *pp* *cre:* . . . . . .

a tempo
cantando
FAL
gril - lo che vibra entro l'uom brillo. Trilla ogni fi - bra in
wink - ing a gob-lin keeps you drink-ing. Trill-ing its si - ren-
a tempo
scen . . . . do . . . . sem . . . . . pre . . . . poco . . . . a . .
cor, l'alle-gro e - tere al trillo guiz - za e il giocon - do
song, the wine thrills us all, cru-el or ten - der. And a world con-
poco . . . .
glo - bo squi - li - bra una de-men-za tril - lan - te! E il
-tent - ed, de - lir - ious in its fol - ly, de - ment - ed, shall
tril-lo inva - de il mon - do!!!
will - ing-ly sur - ren - der!
f
ff

ALL.º AGITATO 𝅗𝅥 = 80
QUICKLY (interrupting Falstaff's happy musings)
Q
Reve - ren - - za. La bella A - li - ce...
I am hon - ored! Fair Mis-tress A - lice. . . . (rising violently)
FAL
Al dia - vo - lo
Go, take her to
(11)
ALL.º AGITATO 𝅗𝅥 = 80
pp
mf
FAL
te con A - li - ce bel - la! Ne ho pie - ne le bi -
Hell and re-main there for - ev - er! The Dev - il will a -
f
p
QUIC.
Voi sie - te er - ra - to....
You are mis - tak - en..
FAL
- sac - cie! Ne ho pie - ne le bu - del - la! Un
-dore her . . . for me she is too clev - er. I
f
p

can-che-ro!! Sen-to an-cor le cor-
know her now, and my ears are still
f
p
-na-te di quel-l'ir-co ge-lo-so! Ho an-
ach-ing From the screams of her hus-band, My
-cor l'os-sa ar-rem-ba-te d'esser ri-ma-sto
brok-en bones still shak-ing, Tossed in a ti-ny
3
p
senza misura
presto
curvo, come una buona la-ma di Bil-bà-o, nel-lo spa-zio d'un panie-rin di
bas-ket, my bod-y bent as if it were A blade of Span-ish steel, hilt to point and head to
senza misura
col canto

a tempo
FAL
da-ma! Con quel tu-fo!- E quel cal-do!- Un
heel! Mad(12)-men shriek-ing! Lin - en reek-ing! I,
f
a tempo
FAL
uom del-la mia tem-pra, che in u-no stil-li-ci - dio con-
melt-ing like a can-dle In heat that e-ven Sa - tan would
p
p
FAL
-ti-nuo si di-stempra! Poi,............ quan-do fui ben
find too hot to han-dle! Then, while I'd burn like
f
f
FAL
cot-to, ro-ven-te, incan-de-scente, m'han tuf-fa - to nel-
tin-der And slow-ly would turn to cin-der, In the end they would
f

(Alice, Meg, Ann, Ford, Cajus, and Fenton are seen hiding behind a building to the left. They listen intently, emerging in turn from their hiding-place.)
QUIC.
Essa è inno - cen - te, essa è inno -
But she is blame-less, com-plete-ly
l'ac-qua. Ca - naglie!!!
drown me! Those ras-cals!
f
p
(feverishly)
- cen - te. Pren - de - te ab - ba - glio... La col - pa è di quei
blame - less! She could do noth - ing... The fault lay with those
Vat - te - ne!!
Out with you!
fan - ti malaugu - ra - ti! A - li - ce piange, ur - la,
duff - ers whom she de - spis - es! She is in tor-ment, cry-ing
pp

Q
in - vo - ca i san - - ti. Po - - ve - ra
Ah, how she suf - - fers! Un - - hap - py
pp
Q
donna!! V'a - - - - ma. Leg-
wom-an! See here, she
mf
(She takes a letter from her pocket and hands it to Falstaff who starts reading it.)
Q
- ge - te.
loves you!
ppp
ff

ALICE (in the background, whispering to the others)
pp
(Legge.
Read-ing?
NANNETTA
Vedrai che ci ri-
His mien looks much more
FORD (softly)
Legge.
Reading!
p
L'uomo non si cor-reg-ge.
Man nev-er sheds his fol-ly.
- casca.
jol-ly.
MEG
(to Alice, alerted by a sign from Quickly)
Na-scondi-ti.
Con-ceal your-self!

Dr. CAJUS
senza misura
Ri-leg-ge.
He's read-ing.
FORD
Ri-leg-ge.- L' esca inghiotte.)
He's nib-bling and will swal-low!
FAL.
(re-reading the letter with great concentration)
T'aspette-rò nel par-to Re-al,
"I shall a-wait you on the stroke of
col canto
FAL
a mez-za-not-te. Tu verrai tra-ve-sti-to da CACCIA-TO-RE NE-RO
mid-night in the park. You will come quite a-lone, in the guise of the Black Hunts-man,
QUIC.
A-mor, a-ma il mi-ste-
Mys-te-rious but en-tranc-
FAL
al-la quer-cia di Her-ne.
to the Oak of Herne."

ANDANTE ♩= 80
-ro. Per ri-ve-der-vi, A-li-ce, si val d'u-na leggen-da po-po-
-ing! Long-ing to see you, fear-ing to fail, A-lice re-called an an-cient
ANDANTE ♩= 80
(13) pp
-lar. Quel-la quer-cia è un luo-go da tre-
tale. You should know the Oak of Herne is
legg. e stacc.
p
(long silence) cupo
-gen-da. Il CAC-CIATO-RE NE-RO s'è im-
haunt-ed. Clad all in black, a hunt-er was found
lunga pausa
-pe-so ad un suo ra-mo. V'na chi
hang-ing from its branch-es. Weird and
ppp

ten.
Q
cre - de ve - der - lo ri - com - pa -
ee - rie, his ghost still is seen at
ten.
ff
pp
- rir....
night.
(taking Quickly by the arm and guiding her inside the Inn)
parlate
FAL
Entriamo. Là si discor-re meglio.
We'll en-ter. Let us con-verse in pri-vate!
leggerissime e stacc.
SEMPRE LO STESSO TEMPO ♩= 80
(starts to tell him the legend while entering the Inn)
Quando il rin-toc-co del-la mezza-
Oft when the chimes of twelve-o'clock have
Narrami la tua frasca.
Tell me that fearsome story!
morendo
SEMPRE LO STESSO TEMPO ♩= 80
(14)

(advancing in a huddle with the others, grotesquely and mysteriously imitating Quickly's narration)
ALI.
voce grossa
Quan-do il rin-toc-co della mezza-
Oft when the chimes of twelve-o'clock have
not-te cu-po si spar-ge nel silen-te or-ror, sor-gon gli
FORD sound-ed, Leav-ing the world in dark and si-lent gloom, De-mons and
Ci casca.
He's bit-ing!
ppp
-not-te Cu-po si spar-ge nel silente or-ror, Sor-gon gli
sound-ed, Leav-ing the world in dark and si-lent gloom, De-mons and
(Her voice is trailing off.)
morendo
spirti vagabon-di a frot-te....
ghosts will hold the Oak sur-round-ed...
p
(darkly)
cupo
spirti vagabon-di a frot-te E..... vien nel par-co il nero Caccia-
ghosts will hold the Oak sur-round-ed: Back comes the Hunt-er a-ris-ing from his

A
-tor.
tomb
E-gli cammi-na
He is ap-proach-ing
ppp
A
len-to, len-to, len-to, Nel gran le-tar-go del-la sepol-
slow-ly, slow-ly, slow-ly, As though en-tranced and walk-ing with-out
A
-tu-ra. S'avan-za li-vi-do...
NAN.
wak-ing, His bones are clat-ter-ing. . .
Oh! che spa-
Phan-tom un-
pp
cres.

MEG
- ven - to!
- ho - ly!
Sen - to già il bri - vi - do del - la pa -
I feel my blood con - geal and I am
- u - ra!
shak - ing.
f
ppp
morendo
(resuming her natural tone of voice)
sempre a tempo
ALLEGRETTO ♩= 138
con brio
ALI.
Fan - do - nie che ai bam - bo - li Rac -
A fan - cy-free, a fair - y tale, For
ALLEGRETTO ♩= 138
con eleganza
p
- con - tan le non - ne Con lun - ghi pre -
chil - dren to pon - der, To set them on their

A
-am-bo-li, Per far-li dor-mir............... Ven-det-ta di
NAN.
mer-ry way And lull them to sleep! Our hunt-er will
Ven-det-ta di
MEG
Our hunt-er will
Ven-det-ta di
Our hunt-er will
f
A
don-ne Non de-ve fal-lir.
won-der, Our meet-ing we'll keep!
ANDANTE (come prima) ♩=80
N
don-ne Non de-ve fal-lir.
won-der, Our meet-ing we'll keep!
M
don-ne Non de-ve fal-lir.
won-der, Our meet-ing we'll keep!
ANDANTE (come prima) ♩=80
(15)
p
(resuming her narration)
A
S'avan-za li-vi-do e il pas-so con-
...his bones are clat-ter-ing, he's reach-ing his

A
ver - ge Al tronco ove e - sa - lò l'a - ni - ma
sta - tion Where long a - go his life sad - ly had
A
pra - va. Sbu - can le Fa - te.- Sul - la fronte e -
end - ed. See, from his fore - head, to his con-ster -
A
dim.
morendo
gl'er - ge Due cor - na lun - ghe, lun - ghe, lun - ghe...
na - tion, Two horns keep - grow - ing, grow - ing, grow - ing . . .
dim.
pp morendo
ALLEGRO 𝅗𝅥=138
FORD
Bra - va! Quel - le cor - na sa - ranno la mia
Splen-did! May these horns bring me nev-er-end - ing
ALLEGRO 𝅗𝅥=138
f
p

(to Ford)
(calmly)
A
FOR
Ba - da! tu pur ti me-ri-ti
Now re - pent your in - an - i - ty!
gio - ia!
glad - ness!
dolce
tr
f
p
Qual-che ca-sti-ga - to - ia!
You and your jeal-ous mad-ness!
Per - do-na... Ri-co-
For - give me . . . I am
Ma guai se ancor ti co - glie
Be - ware lest your sus - pi - cion
- no - sco i miei de - me - ri-ti...
cured of my in - san - i-ty!

LO STESSO MOVIMENTO ♩=138
pp leggiero
Quel - la ma-nia fe - - ro - ce Di cer-car dentro il
Should once a-gain dis - - cov - er In the shell of a.
LO STESSO MOVIMENTO ♩=138
leggiero
pp
m.s.
(16)
gu-scio d'u-na no - ce L'a - man - - - te di tua
nut a se-cret lov - er To mar your dis-po -
p
Recit.
-mo - glie.- Ma il tem-po strin-ge e vuol fan-ta-sia
- si - tion! But time is fleet-ing. Let's keep our wits a -
Recit.
MEG
le - sta. Nan -
- bout - us! Now,
FEN.
Affrettiam.
You are right.
Concer - tiam la ma-sche-ra - ta.
or the play will start with-out us!

A TEMPO SEMPRE ♩=138
A
NAN.
net_ta.
Ann-ie!
Ec_co_la qua!
At your com-mand!
A TEMPO SEMPRE ♩=138
(17)
p
Sa_rai la Fa_ta Re_gi_na del_le
You'll play the part of the Queen of all the
Fa_te, in bianca ve_sta........Chiusa in candi_do
Fair-ies. Your roy-al man-tle shall be white And your
vel, cin_ta di ro_se.
veil gir-dled by ros-es.
E can_te_
In ten-der

N
-rò pa - - ro - le armonï - o - - - se.
song my heart sweet-ly re - pos- - - es.
(18)
ALI.
(to Meg)
Tu la ver - de sa -
You, dear Meg, clad in
A
-rai Nin-fa sil - va - - na,
green, Will be the Wood - - Nymph,
A
pausa
E la co - ma - re Quic - kly u - na be -
And our dear Mis-tress Quick - ly shall be a
(19)

(The evening falls. The scene turns darker
1º TEMPO ANCORA ♩= 138
leggero
A
-fa - na.
sor - ceress.
A - vrò con me dei
A. host of ti - ny
NAN.
(happily)
3
A me-ra - - vi-glia!
Ah, this is price-less!
1º TEMPO ANCORA ♩= 138
leggero assai
pp
and darker.)
put - ti Che fin-ge-ran fol - let-ti E spi-ri-tel-li E dia-vo -
tots will play In most de-light-ful roun-de-lay As ghost-ly pix-ies
-let-ti E pi-pi-strelli E far-fa - rel - li. Su Fal-staff ca-muf -
clad in grey And dev-ils who will haunt him. And then we shall as -
-fa-to in man - to e cor-ni Ci sca-glie-re-mo
-sault our love - lorn hunt-er And mer-ci-less-ly
f

A
tut _ ti
E lo tem_pe_ste _ re_mo Finch'abbia confes_
taunt him.
Un-til the old of - fend-er Is read - y to sur-
NAN.
Tut _ ti! tut _ ti!
Haunt him! Taunt him!
MEG
Tut _ ti! tut _ ti!
Haunt him! Taunt him!
FEN.
Tut _ ti! tut _ ti!
Haunt him! Taunt him!
f
pp
f
pp
A
portando la voce
con grazia
_sa _ ta la sua perver_si _ tà.................. Poi ci smasche _ re _
- ren - der And eat his hum-ble pie Then, on - ly then, we'll
f
pp
pp
A
_re _ _ _ mo E pria che il ciel rag _
free him When quite con - trite we
3
3

A
-gior - ni, La giu - li - - va bri - ga - ta
see him. Gai-ly— laugh- - ing we'll flee him,
f
p
A
Se ne ritor - ne - rà.
MEG
Bid him a fond good - bye!
Vien se - ra. Rin-ca-
Let's leave now, it is
p
A
L'appunta - men-to è alla quer - cia di Her - ne.
We are a - greed when we meet at the oak - tree.
M
-siam.
FEN.
late.
È in -
At

NAN.
A mera - vi - glia! Oh! che alle - gro spaven - to!
Ah, what an an - tic! How di-vine and ro-man - tic!
EN
- te - so.
mid-night!
(Alice, Ann and Fenton exit to the left, Meg to the right.)
ALI.
Ad - di - o.
Fare - well now!
N
Ad - di - o.
Fare - well now!
MEG
(to Alice and Ann)
Ad - di - o.
Till mid-night!
FEN
Ad - di - o.
Fare - well now!
pp
pp
cres.

pp
(Quickly, leaving the inn, notices Ford and Cajus in confidential conversation. She stops to listen.)
ALI. (to Meg, shouting)
Provvedi le lan - ter - ne.
Do not for-get the lan-terns!
(20) pp
FORD (to Cajus, softly)
Non du - bitar, tu spo - serai mia fi - glia.
You may - be sure. Soon you will wed my daugh - ter.
FOR
Ram - men - ti be - ne il suo tra - - ve - sti
Do you re - mem - ber the dress she will be

Dr C.

Cin - ta di ro - se, il vel
Belt trimmed with ros - es, white her

FORD

-men - to?
wear - ing?

sempre p

ALI. (calling from offstage, left)

Non ti scordar le maschere.
You will pro-vide the dom-i-noes!

MEG (from offstage right)

No, certo. Nè tu le raga-
They're read-y. You bring the bones and

Dr C

bian-co e la ve-sta.
veil and her gar-ment.

p pp

M

-nel - le!
rat - tles.

FORD (continuing his conversation with Cajus)

Io già di - spo - si la
My plan is laid, its suc -

(21) p

FOR
re - te mi - a. Sul finir del - la
-cess is cer - tain: Well dis-guised by a
FOR
fe - sta Verre - te a me col volto rico - perto Es - - sa da un
hood you will come to me as soon as all is o-ver. Ann will be
m.d.
m.s.
FOR
vel, tu da un man - tel fra - te - sco
there, still hid - den by her veil and
D.C.
Siam d'ac-
Fine sug-
FOR
E vi be - ne - di - rò co - me due spo - - si.
I shall be - stow my bless - ing on the two of you.
pp

QUIC.
(giving the two men a telling look, then disappearing rapidly to the right)
(Stai fre - sco!)
(No ques - tion!)
- cor - do.
- ges - tion!
22
sempre pp
NAN.
senza misura
(from offstage)
Che c'è? Che c'è?
I'm here. What is it?
QUIC.
senza misura
Presto (from offstage right)
Nannetta! Ohè! Nannetta! Ohè!
Oh, Ann! Pst! My Ann-ie, pst!
senza misura col canto
p
(from offstage)
È prepara - ta....
It-nev-er-var-ies!
Prepara la canzone della Fa - ta.
You know the song of the Queen of the Fair - ies?

ALI.
(offstage)
N
Tu, non tar - dar.
You-will-be-late!
pp
QUIC.
(from faraway)
morendo
(Night has fallen.)
Chi prima arri - va,a - spet - ta.
The soon-er there, the bet - ter!
pp
pp
stacc.
pp
pp
pp
m.d.
8
stacc.
ppp

Act Three

Part Two

Windsor Park.

In the center, the Oak of Herne. To the rear, indications of a gully. Thick foliage. Bushes in bloom. It is night.

In the distance the horn-calls of the foresters are heard.

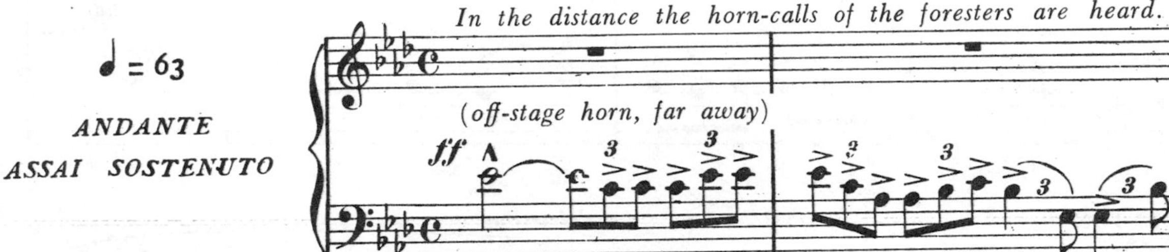

Gradually the forest is brightened by moonlight. (Fenton, later Ann disguised as Queen

of the Fairies. Later Alice, not disguised, carrying a hood over one arm and a mask in her hand.

Mrs. Quickly carrying the paraphernalia of her disguise as a witch, including a broomstick. Later Meg, garbed in green veils and wearing a mask.)

m.s.
tr
pp
6.
(enter Fenton)
f
morendo
lunga
FENTON
dolcissimo
Dal labbro il canto esta_sï_a _ to
From burn-ing lips my song of love en-
(23)
pp
dolciss.
FEN
dolciss.
pp
vo_la.......Pei silenzi not_turni e va lonta _ _ no E alfin ri-
-chant-ed, Throughthedarkofthe night so gently call _ _ ing, Shall fly be-
8

sempre dolciss.
dim. dolce
-trova un altro labbro u - ma - no Che gli ri - sponde col-la sua pa -
-yond to where the stars are fall - ing, Un-til at last my ar-dent plea is
pp
poco più marcato
- ro - la. Allor la no - ta che non è più
grant - ed. Out of the long and lone-ly night a -
(24)
p
sottovoce
so - la Vibra di gioia in un accor-do ar - ca - no E innamo - -
-round me A ten-der song, a ray of light con - found me. Oh, mag-ic

FEN
-ran-do l'aer an-te-lu-ca-no Con al-tra
song whose sounds al-ways will bind me, Oh, guide my
ppp
FEN
dolcissimo
vo-ce...............al suo fonte ri-vo - - - -
loved one till at last she will find
dolcissimo
ppp
FEN
-la......................
me!
p
p
Quivi ripi-glia suon, ma..... la sua
Once you have brought her here, her-ald so
FEN
cu-ra.............. Tende sempre ad u-nir chi lo di-su-na.........
ten-der, You will soon have to die: You must sur-ren-der.
dim. e poco allarg.

con espressione
EN
.... Co - sì ba - ciai la di - sï - a - ta boc - -
Un - to the si - lence of our burn - ing kiss - -
f
pp
- ca! Boc - ca ba - -
- es. Just kiss me
(25)
ppp
NANNETTA
(from off-stage)
An - zi rin -
Trust in the
- cia - - ta non per - de ven - tu - - ra.
soon, and you al - ways will do it!
(coming closer)
dolce
- no - va co - me fa....... la lu - - - - -
moon, love will al - ways re - new
(running in the direction from which he heard Ann's voice)
Ma il can - to
Yes, song will
pp

(*All of a sudden, Alice steps between the lovers. She is not disguised and carries a hood over one arm and a mask in her hand.*)

ALICE

f

Nos - si -
Just a

(*enter Ann, disguised as the Queen of the Fairies*)

N

- - - na, co - me fa la lu - na.
it, al - ways will re - new it!

FEN

f

muor nel ba - cio che lo toc - ca.
die on lips that are u - nit - ed.

p

ALL.° VIVO 𝅗𝅥 = 132

(*Quickly has followed Alice, carrying the paraphernalia of her disguise as a witch, including a stick and a horror-mask.*)

A

- gnore! - Tu indossa questa cappa.
mo-ment! Put on this robe, and hur-ry!

Al -
Don't

N

Lasciati fare.
I'll tell you lat-er.

(*puts on the robe, assisted by Alice and Ann*)

FEN

Che vuol dir ciò?
But what is this?

ALL.° VIVO 𝅗𝅥 = 132

f

f

(giving Fenton the mask)
(Fenton adjusts the robe and mask.)
-lac-cia.
wor-ry!
(26) ppp leggero
legg.
(helping Fenton to don the mask)
ALI.
parlante
Il tradi -
The wil-y
NAN.
(admiring Fenton)
È un fraticel sgu-sciato dalla Trap - - pa.
He looks like one es - caping from a con - vent.
ppp leggero e staccato

A
-men - to che Ford ne mi - nac-cia Tor-nar de - ve in suo
ruse that my hus - band is plan-ning, let us use it and
A
scorno e in nostro a-iu - to.
turn it back up-on him!
Ub-bi-di-sci
Take my word! Be
FEN.
Spie - ga-te-vi.
A ruse, you say?
A
pre-sto e mu - to.
clev-er! O-bey me!
L'oc-ca-sï-o-ne co-me
The i-ron's hot, we'll strike it
sempre e staccato
(to Quickly)
A
vie - ne scap-pa.
now or nev-er.
Chi ve-sti-raï da fin-ta
As bride to be whom have you

spo - sa?
cho - sen?
QUICKLY
Un ga - io la - dron na - su - to Che ab -
That rogue with the big red nose Who has
MEG
(entering from the rear, wearing a mask and a disguise of green veils)
(to Alice)
Ho na - sco - sto i fol -
All the chil - dren are
- borre il Dot - tor Ca - - jo.
raised the Doc - tor's dan - - - der.
- let - ti lungo il fos - so. Siam pron - te.
hid - ing in the bush - es. We're read - y.

ALI.
(listening)
Zit - to...
Si-lence!
mf
A
Viene il pez-zo
Hear the hap-py
cres.
(The women and Fenton scurry off to the left.)
A
gros-so.
hunt-er!
Vi - a!..
Van-ish!
NAN.
Vi - a!..
Hur-ry!
MEG
Vi - a!..
Van-ish!
QUIC.
Vi - a!..
Hur-ry!
(27)
f
ff

(At the stroke of midnight, Falstaff enters cautiously from the right. He is wearing an enormous pair of antlers and a wide cloak.)

FALSTAFF

U - na,
One, —

(28)

(suona mezzanotte)
(midnight chimes)

PIÙ MOSSO ♩ = 100

pp

du - e, tre, quat - tro, cin - que,
two, — three, four, — five, —

FAL
sei, set_te bot_te, Ot_to, no_ve,
six, sev-en strokes Eight, nine,
ppp
ppp
FAL
die_ci, un_di_ci, do_di_ci.-
ten, e-lev-en, twelve.
Mezza_
It is
mf
COME PRIMA ♩ = 60
FAL
_notte.
mid-night.
COME PRIMA ♩ = 72
(29)
ppp
(noticing Herne's Oak)
FAL
Quest'è la quer_cia.-
Here is the oak-tree.
pp sempre

Numi proteg - ge - te - mi!
Might-y pow-ers, stay with me!
PIÙ MOSSO ♩ = 100
Gio - ve! Tu per amor d'Eu - ro - pa ti tra - sfor -
Help me, Jove, who be-came a bull wear-ing horns for
tr
pp
PIÙ MOSSO ♩ = 100
(30) ppp
- ma - sti in bo - - - - ve; Porta - sti
love of fair Eu - ro - - - - pa. I need your
pp
cor - - na. - I Nu - mi c'insegnan la mode - stia.
coun - - sel. The Gods teach us grace and res-ig-na - tion,
marcate
pp

ALLEGRO ♩ = 116
FAL
L'a - mo - - - re me - ta -
as love to hum - ble
ALLEGRO ♩ = 116
f
(Alice appears
in the rear.)
animando un poco
(listening)
-morfo - sa un uom in u - na be - - stia.
beast will turn the glo - ry of cre - a - - - tion.
f
(31)
pp animando un poco
pp
O - do un so - a - ve pas - so!
Is this her ten - der foot - step?
p sempre e staccato
(goes towards her)
A - li - ce! Amor ti chia - ma!
She's near me, drawn by my pas - sion, . . .

ALI.
(approaching Falstaff)
Sir John!
Sir John!
Sir John!
Sir John!
Vie _ ni! l'amor m'in _ fiamma! Sei la mia da _ ma! Sei la mia
. . . near me, for me to cap-ture! Show me com - pas - sion! Yield to my
O sfa _ vil _ lan - te a - mor!
Oh blaz-ing flame of love!
(vainly trying to embrace her)
damma! Vie - ni! Già fremo e
rap-ture! Hear me . . . an - swer my
(always avoiding his embraces)
Sir John!
Sir John!
fer _ vo! Sono il tuo ser _ vo! Sono il tuo cer _ vo imbizzar _
crav-ing! You are my doe and I am your stag, rant - ing and

FAL
-ri - to. Ed or piovan tar - tu-fi, ra - fa-ni, fi-
rav - ing. In a show-er of truf-fles, rad - ish-es, and
FAL
-noc-chi!!! E sien la mia pa - stu-ra! E amor tra-
cus-tard the sky pro-vide the sup-per and love the
ALI.
No...
Wait!
FAL
-boc-chi!!.. Siam so - li...
mus-tard! A - lone here. . . .

Qua nel - la sel - va den - sa Mi se - gue
There in the wood be - - hind us is Mis - tress
Meg.
Page.
FAL.
È dop-pia l'av-ven - tu - ra! Ven - ga an - che
Good For-tune has com - bined us all on one
con forza
L
lei! Squar - ta - - te - mi
stage! Now both of you,
(32)
ff

FAL
Co - me un camo - scio a men - sa!! Sbra - na - temi!!!......
cut me in two! Di - vide me! Dis - mem - ber me!
FAL
..... Cupido al fin mi ricom - pensa! Io t'a - mo!, io t'a - mo!, io t'a - mo!,
Un-to my al - tar you shall guide me! I love you! I love you! I love you,
ALI.
senza misura
(pretending to be frightened)
Un gri - do! Ahimè!
Good Heav-ens, a scream!
MEG
(offstage)
A - iu - to!!!
Oh help me!
(appearing unmasked but staying in the shadow)
Vien la tre -
The host un -
FAL
t'a - - mo!
love you.
col canto

a tempo
A
Ahimè!
A-las!
(flees)
Fug-gia-mo!
Let's flee them!
Il ciel per-
I pray to
M
-gen - da!
-ho - ly!
(terrified)
FAL
Do-ve?
Where to?
a tempo
mf
A
(runs off to the right)
-doni al mio pecca - to!
God for my sal-va - tion!
(hiding near the oak-tree)
FAL
Il dia-vo-lo non
I nev-er have a
f
FAL
vuol ch'io sia dan - na - to.
chance to court dam - na - tion!
mf cres.
ff

NANNETTA
LARGO
(offstage)
(33)
LARGO
ppp
Nin-fe! El-fi!
Elf-ins! Fair-ies!
N
Sil-fi! Do-ri-di! Si-re - - ne! L'a-stro de-gl'incan-
Pix-ies! Spir-its all, oh hear me! Cast-ing his mag-ic
-te-si-mi in cie-lo è sor - - - to. Sor-
spell on us, the moon is smil - - - ing. A-
(She appears among the trees.)
p
-ge - - - - - te! Om-bre se - re- -
-rise now, shad-ows who cheer
p
ppp

-ne!
me!
WOMEN'S VOICES (from far away)
ppp
Nin - fe! Sil - fi! Si - re
Pix - ies! Fair - ies! And elf
FALSTAFF
sottovoce (in a panic, throws himself to the ground, face down)
So-no le Fa-te. Chi le guarda è morto.
Un ho ly de mons! No one lives who sees them.
-ne.
-ins!
legg.
(34) ppp
(Ann now is fully visible, disguised as Queen of the Fairies. A number of girls are dressed as white and as blue fairies. Falstaff remains on the ground, motionless.)
ALI.
(cautiously stepping forth with some of the fairies)
p
I - nol -
Fol- low

(noticing Falstaff also and pointing him out to the others)
A
p
_triam.
Ste _ so al
NAN.
me! (cautiously advancing from the opposite side, noticing Falstaff) on the
E _ gli è là.
There he lies,
A
suol...
ground.
N
Lo con _ fon _ de il ter _
He is dy _ ing with
pp
(They all advance stealthily.)
N
_ ror.
fear.

ALI.
Non ri-
You be
FAIRIES
Si na-scon-de:
He is hid-ing.
-diam!
still!
(instructing the fairies with regard to their actions, places, etc. while Alice exits rapidly to the left)
NAN.
Tutte quì, dietro a me...
Do you know what to do?
cominciam...
Watch my cue!
Non ridiam!
Yes, we will.
Tocca a
We're with
(A group of fairies form a circle around Ann. Another, taller group gathers to the left.)
te.
you.
dim. e rall.

NANNETTA
LO STESSO MOVIMENTO ♩=63
LO STESSO MOVIMENTO ♩=63
(35)
Sul fil d'un sof_fio e_
A gleam in shim-m'ring
ppp leggeriss. e stacc.
corda sola
dolciss.
N
_te _ si_o
sil _ ver glow
Scor_re_te a_gi_li
And bathed in mist-y
dolciss.
portando la voce
N
lar _ ve,
lath _ er,
Fra i rami un ba_glior
O-ver the vale and
N
ce _ si _ o
hill be - low
D'al_ba lu_na_re ap_
Elves of the night fore-

_par _ ve. Dan _ za _ te! e il pas_so
_gath - er. And gent - ly, gent - ly we
blan_do Mi _ su _ ri un blan _ do suon,
sway As we dance__ be-neath the moon,
Le magiche ac_cop _ pian _ do......................... Ca_ro_le al _ la can _
Smil-ing at him from far a-way. ———— We sing our haunt - ing

N
_zon.
tune.
CHORUS OF FAIRIES
ppp
(Slow and graceful dance of the little fairies)
La sel _ va dor
The for - est slum
(36)
pp
levare corda sola
_ me
bers
e sper _ de incen
with-out the slight-
so ed om
est mo
bra;
tion,
e par nel _ l'a _ er
A world be - neath an
pp

denso un ver - de a - si - lo in fon - do al

o-cean, A par - a - dise be - low the

p

poco allarg.

NANNETTA

COME PRIMA

dolciss.

Er - riam sot - to la

The blos - soms here and

mar.

sea.

COME PRIMA

pp leggeriss. e stacc.

(37) ancora corda sola

N

lu - na

yon - der,

Sce - glien - do fior da

A - wak - ened by our

dolce

N

fio - re, Ogni corol - la in co - re........................

danc - es View us with sleep-y glanc - es, ______

tr

N
sempre dolce
dim.
tr
pp
(38)
.... Porta la sua for_tu_na. Coi gi - gli e le vï -
Rubbing their eyes in won_der. The ros - es tell us a
_o _ le Scri_viam........ de' no _ mi ar _ ca - - ni,
sto - ry Of love and sweet sur - ren - - der,
Dal_le fa_ta - te ma - ni
Lil - ies so proud and slen - der
.... Germo_gli_no pa_ro - le.
Will sing _ of might and glo - ry.

N
Pa_ro_le al_lu - mi - na - te
Trust in their mag - ic pow - ers,
N
Di pu_ro argen - to e d'or, Carmi e ma_
Trust in their friend - ship true! Know-ing a
N
_lì - - - - - e. Le
se - - - - - cret, the
N
Fa - te hanno per ci - fre.................. i
flow - ers Al-ways con-fide it to

POCO PIÙ ANIMATO.
morendo
N
fior......
you.
CHORUS OF FAIRIES
(gathering flowers)
Mo_via_mo ad u_na ad u_na
Now slow - ly let us wan-der
POCO PIÙ ANIMATO.
pp
Sot _ to il luna _ re al _ bor, Ver_so la quer _ cia
There in the shad - ows blue, To the big oak - tree
p
(During this chorus, all the Fairies slowly approach the oak.)
NAN.
dolciss.
Le Fa _ te han _ no per
The flow - ers al - ways
bru _ na Del ne_ro Cac _ cia _ tor.
yon - der Where we pay Herne his due.
pp

(coming from upstage left, followed by Alice in mask, Meg as the green wood-nymph, Quickly as a witch, Dr. Cajus in a grey cloak, not masked, Pistol disguised as a satyr, Ford undisguised, Fenton in black robe and mask. Several others wear phantastic costumes, carrying lanterns of various shapes and sizes.)

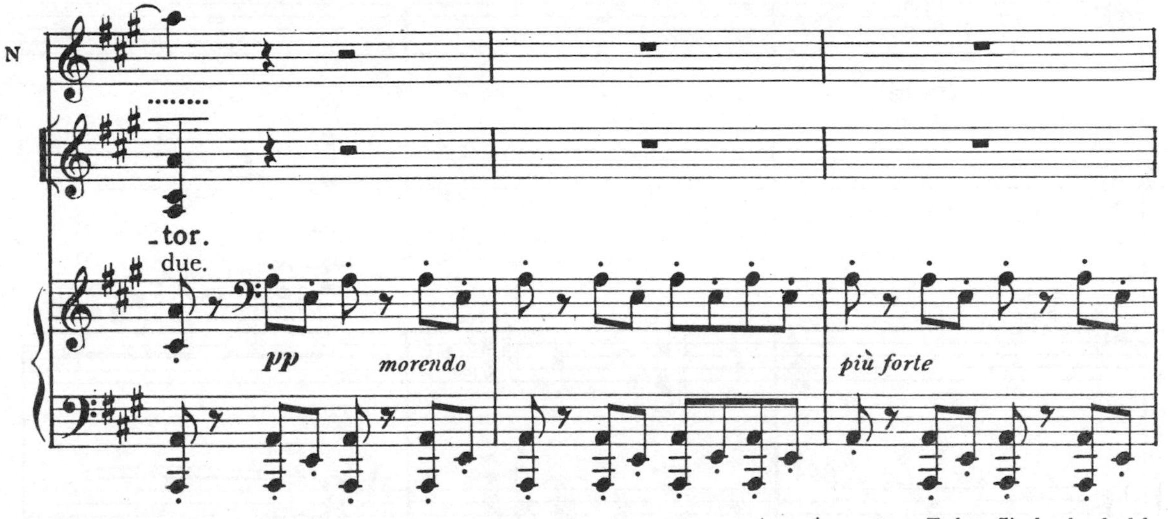

N

_tor.
due.

pp *morendo* *più forte*

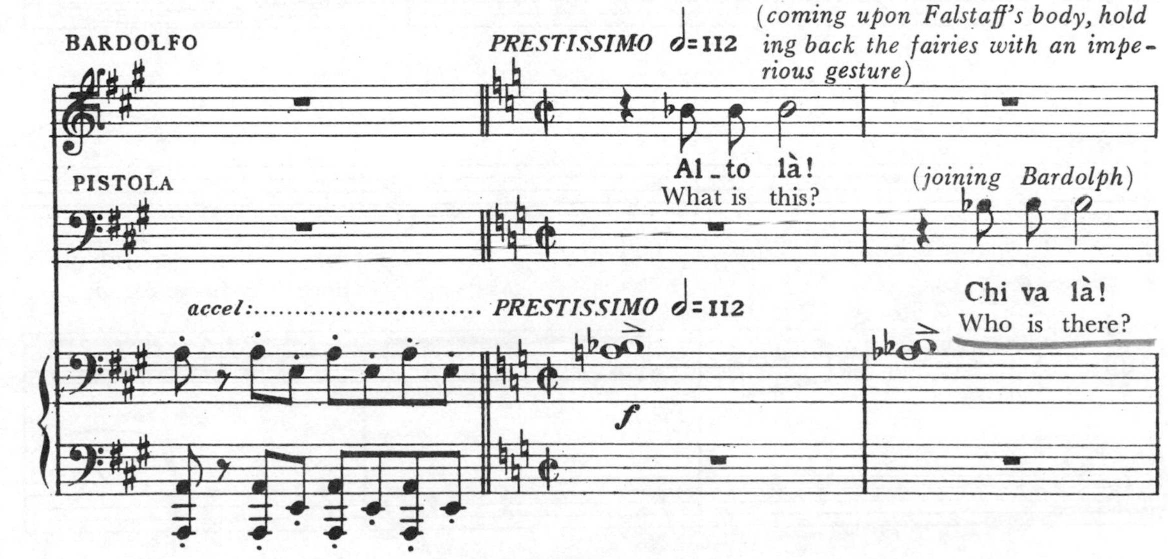

BARDOLFO

PRESTISSIMO 𝅗𝅥 = 112 *(coming upon Falstaff's body, holding back the fairies with an imperious gesture)*

Al_to là!
What is this?

PISTOLA

(joining Bardolph)

Chi va là!
Who is there?

accel:.......................... *PRESTISSIMO* 𝅗𝅥 = 112

f

ALI.
C'è un uom!
A man!
NAN.
C'è un uom!
A man!
MEG
C'è un uom!
A man!
QUIC.
(touching Falstaff with her broomstick)
C'è un uomo!
A hu-man!
FAL.
Pietà!
A-las!
FAIRIES
Un uom!
A man!
ff
FORD
Cor - nu - to co - me un
His horns be-speak de -
fp
mf

R.
bu - e!
- fi - ance.
Ro - ton - do co - me un po - mo!
He must be born of gi - ants.
BARD.
Gros - so come u - na na - ve!
Fit to serve on a plat - ter.
f
(kicking Falstaff)
B
Al - za - ti o - là!
FAL. Up with you, a - rise!
(lifting his head)
Porta - temi u - na gru - e! Non
PIST.
With-out the help of sci-ence . . . I
Al - za - ti o - là!
Up with you, a - rise!
f

QUIC.
È cor - rot - to!
He's a mon - ster!
FAL
posso.
FORD can-not!
È troppo gra - ve.
A weight-y mat-ter!
CHORUS OF FAIRIES
È cor
He's a
ALI.
È im - pu - ro!
What pol - lu - tion!
NAN.
È im - pu - ro!
What pol - lu - tion!
MEG
È im - pu - ro!
What pol - lu - tion!
BARD.
(with gestures of a sorcerer)
Si
Let's
- rot - to!
mon - ster!
È im - pu - ro!
What pol - lu - tion!

(aside to Ann while Dr. Cajus is looking for someone. Fenton and Quickly are hiding Ann.)
ALI.
(E _ vi_ta il tuo pe _
Dan - ger is near, be
fac _ cia lo scon _ giu _ ro!
plan his ex - e - cu - tion!
(39) pp
NAN.
- ri_glio. Già il Dottor Ca _ jo ti cer _ ca.
care - ful! Our Doc-tor Ca - - jus is snoop - ing.
Tro -
We
(Shielded by Alice and Quickly, Ann and Fenton withdraw to the rear.)
QUIC.
- via_mo Un na_scon - diglio.
bet - ter go in hid-ing.
Poi torne_re - te le _ sti al mio ri _
But come back here the mo - ment I shall

(Ann and Fenton disappear.)
LO STESSO MOVIMENTO ♩. = 112
Q
_chiamo.)
call you!
(standing over Falstaff's body, pretending to exorcise his spirit)
B
Spi_ri _ tel _ _ li! Fol_let _ ti! Farfa _
Wick-ed serv - ants of Sa - tan! Ghouls and
LO STESSO MOVIMENTO ♩. = 112
f
B
_rel _ _ li! Vam_pi _ _ ri! A _ _ gi _ li in _
gob - lins and de - - mons! Let us de -
B
_set _ ti del pa _ lu _ _ de in _ fer _ na _ le! Punzec _
- ter - mine what to do with this ver - min! Sap his
B
_chiatelo! Or_ti_cheg_giatelo! Marti_riz _zatelo Col grifi a_
san- i -ty! Scratch at his van-i-ty! Hurt his hu-man-i-ty! Pluck him to

(A group of boys dressed as devils, ghouls etc. come running from the rear and pounce on Falstaff. Some of them swing rattles and make noise in other ways. Many of them carry little red lamps.)

ruzzo_la, ruzzo_la, ruzzo_la, ruzzo_la, ruzzo_la, ruzzo_la,
rum-ble and tum-ble and hum-ble him! Jum-ble and rum-ble and tum-ble and
ruzzo_la, ruzzo_la, ruzzo_la, ruzzo_la, ruzzo_la, ruzzo_la,
rum-ble and tum-ble and hum-ble him! Jum-ble and rum-ble and tum-ble and

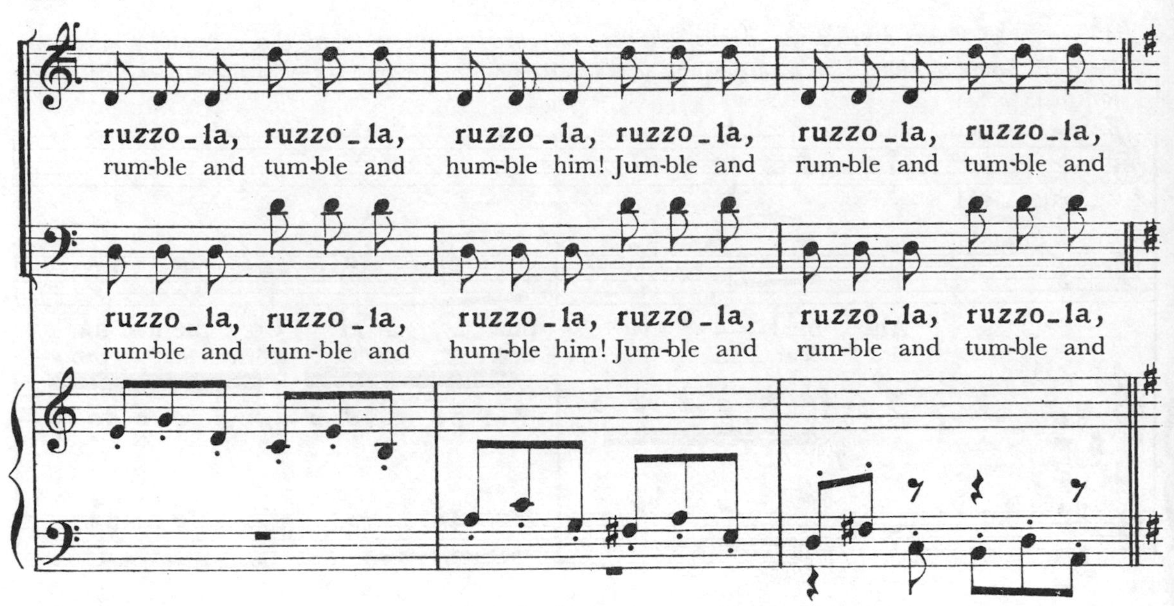

(The children closest to Falstaff pinch his arms and legs, beat his paunch with twigs and torment him in other ways.)

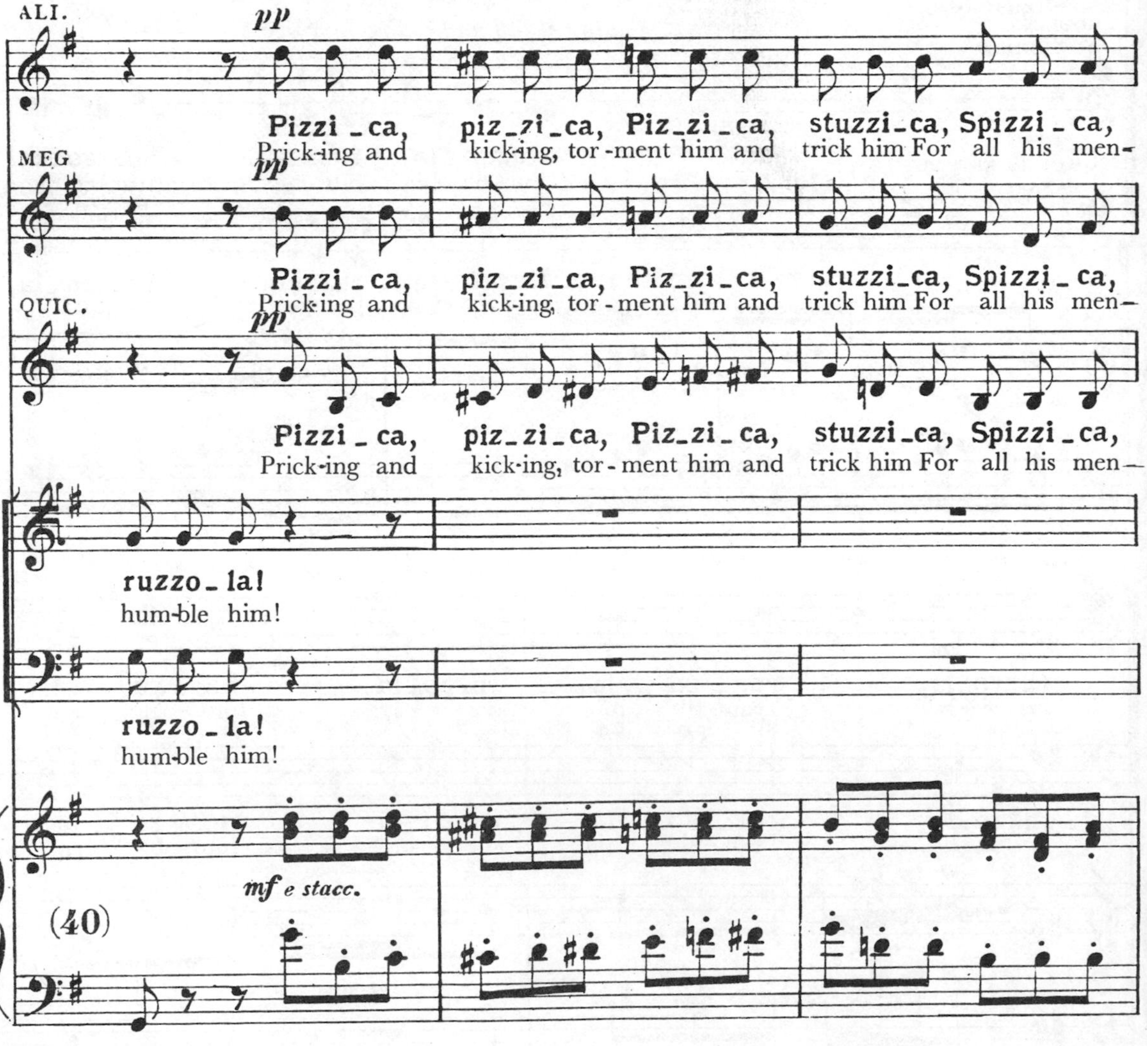

ALI.
pp
Pizzi_ca, piz_zi_ca, Piz_zi_ca, stuzzi_ca, Spizzi_ca,
Prick-ing and kick-ing, tor-ment him and trick him For all his men-
MEG
pp
Pizzi_ca, piz_zi_ca, Piz_zi_ca, stuzzi_ca, Spizzi_ca,
Prick-ing and kick-ing, tor-ment him and trick him For all his men-
QUIC.
pp
Pizzi_ca, piz_zi_ca, Piz_zi_ca, stuzzi_ca, Spizzi_ca,
Prick-ing and kick-ing, tor-ment him and trick him For all his men-
ruzzo_la!
hum-ble him!
ruzzo_la!
hum-ble him!
mf e stacc.
(40)

spizzica, Pungi, spil _ luzzica, pungi, spil _ luz_zi_ca, fin ch'egli ab _
-dac--i-ty and his au - dac-i-ty! Nick-to-the - quick him un - til you will
spizzica, Pungi, spil _ luzzica, pungi, spil _ luz_zi_ca, fin ch'egli ab _
-dac-i-ty and his au - dac-i-ty! Nick-to-the - quick him un - til you will
spizzica, Pungi, spil _ luzzica, pungi, spil _ luz_zi_ca, fin ch'egli ab _
-dac-i-ty and his au - dac-i-ty! Nick-to-the - quick him un - til you will
(The smallest children dance around him, step on him and pull his limbs; Falstaff tries to defend himself, but he cannot move.)
_ ba _ i!
lick him!
_ ba _ i!
lick him!
_ ba _ i!
lick him!
L
Ahi! ahi! ahi! ahi!
Oh! Oh! Oh! Oh!
p
Scrolliam cre_pi _
p De-flate his pro -
(a pandemonium of various noises)
Scrolliam cre_pi _
De-flate his pro -
mf

-ta-co-li Sca-ran-do-le, nacche-re! Di schizzi e di
-pen-si-ty to shock-ing im - men-si-ty! His splen-dor so
-ta-co-li Sca-ran-do-le, nacche-re! Di schizzi e di
-pen-si-ty to shock-ing im - men-si-ty! His splen-dor so
zacche-re Quel-l'o-tre si maco-li. Me-niam scor-ri-
bil-low-y turn slen-der and wil-low-y! The Mas-ter of
zacche-re Quel-l'o-tre si maco-li. Me-niam scor-ri-
bil-low-y turn slen-der and wil-low-y! The Mas-ter of
-bando-le, Dan-zia-mo la tre-sca, Tre-schiam le fa-
Dev-il-ry shall lend you his lanc-es, The fast-er the
-bando-le, Dan-zia-mo la tre-sca, Tre-schiam le fa-
Dev-il-ry shall lend you his lanc-es, The fast-er the

f
-ràndole Sull'ampia ven - tresca. Zan-zàre ed as - silli Vo - late alla
rev-el-ry, the bet-ter the chanc-es To bite him and blight him, to smite and to
f
-ràndole Sull'ampia ven - tresca. Zan-zàre ed as - silli Vo - late alla
rev-el-ry, the bet-ter the chanc-es To bite him and blight him, to smite and to
f
mf
lizza Coi dardi e gli spilli! Ch'ei crepi di stizza, ch'ei crepi di
spite him. So pounce on him, hit him, and trounce him and twit him mf Un-til in the
lizza Coi dardi e gli spilli! Ch'ei crepi di stizza, ch'ei crepi di
spite him. So pounce on him, hit him, and trounce him and twit him Un - til in the
mf stacc.
(The noise suddenly stops.)
stiz-za, ch'ei cre-pi, ch'ei cre - - pi!
end you com-plete-ly de - feat him!
stiz-za, ch'ei cre-pi, ch'ei cre - - pi!
end you com - plete-ly de - feat him!
ff
VUOTA

ALI.
pp
Piz_zi_ca, piz_zi_ca, piz_zi_ca, stuzzi_ca, spizzi_ca,
Prick-ing and kick-ing tor - ment him and trick him For all his men -
MEG.
pp
Piz_zi_ca, piz_zi_ca, piz_zi_ca, stuzzi_ca, spizzi_ca,
Prick-ing and kick-ing tor - ment him and trick him For all his men -
QUIC.
pp
Piz_zi_ca, piz_zi_ca, piz_zi_ca, stuzzi_ca, spizzi_ca,
Pricking and kicking tor - ment him and trick him For all his men -
(41)
pp
A
spizzi_ca, pungi, spil - luzzi_ca, pungi, spil - luzzi_ca, fin ch'egli ab_
-dac-i-ty and his au - dac- i-ty! Nick-to-the - quick him un-til you will
M
spizzi_ca, pungi, spil - luzzi_ca, pungi, spil - luzzi_ca, fin ch'egli ab_
-dac-i-ty and his au - dac- i-ty! Nick-to-the - quick him un-til you will
Q
spizzi_ca, pungi, spil - luzzi_ca, pungi, spil - luzzi_ca, fin ch'egli ab_
-dac-i-ty and his au - daci-ty! Nick-to-the- quick him un-til you will

_bà_i!
lick him!
Coz_za_lo, a_
Tack-le and
_bà_i!
lick him!
Coz_za_lo, a_
Tack-le and
_bà_i!
lick him!
Coz_za_lo, a_
Tack-le and
FAL.
Ahì!
Oh!
ahì!
Oh!
ahì!
Oh!
ahì!
Oh!
mf
Coz_za_lo, a_
Tack-le and
mf
Coz_za_lo, a_
Tack-le and
TENORS
BASSES
mf

A
-iz-za-lo Dai piè al co-cuzzo-lo! Strozzalo, strizzalo! Gli svampi
shack-le him, tat-ter and shat-ter him, Knock him and rock him and sock him and
M
-iz-za-lo Dai piè al co-cuzzo-lo! Strozzalo, strizzalo! Gli svampi
shack-le him, tat-ter and shat-ter him, Knock him and rock him and sock him and
Q
-iz-za-lo Dai piè al co-cuzzo-lo! Strozzalo, strizzalo! Gli svampi
shack-le him, tat-ter and shat-ter him, Knock him and rock him and sock him and
FAL
-iz-za-lo Dai piè al co-cuzzo-lo! Strozzalo, strizzalo! Gli svampi
shack-le him, tat-ter and shat-ter him, Knock him and rock him and sock him and
-iz-za-lo Dai piè al co-cuzzo-lo! Strozzalo, strizzalo! Gli svampi
shack-le him, tat-ter and shat-ter him, Knock him and rock him and sock him and
mf
Ch'ei cre-pi! Ch'ei
De-feat him! De-
mf
Ch'ei cre-pi! Ch'ei
De-feat him! De-

p
l'uzzo_lo! Piz_zi_ca, piz_zi_ca, l'unghia rin_tuzzo_la! piz_zi_ca
- bat-ter him! Prick him and tick-le him for his au-dac-i-ty, Pick-like-a-
p
l'uzzo_lo! Piz_zi_ca, piz_zi_ca, l'unghia rin_tuzzo_la! piz_zi_ca
- bat-ter him! Prick him and tick-le him for his au-dac-i-ty, Pick-like-a-
p
l'uzzo_lo! Piz_zi_ca, piz_zi_ca, l'unghia rin_tuzzo_la! piz_zi_ca
- bat-ter him! Prick him and tick-le him for his au-dac-i-ty, Pick-like-a-
ahi! ahi!
Oh! Oh!
p
l'uzzo_lo! Piz_zi_ca, piz_zi_ca, l'unghia rin_tuzzo_la! piz_zi_ca
- bat-ter him! Prick him and tick-le him for his au-dac-i-ty, Pick-like-a-
p
l'uzzo_lo! Piz_zi_ca, piz_zi_ca, l'unghia rin_tuzzo_la! piz_zi_ca
- bat-ter him! Prick him and tick-le him for his au-dac-i-ty, Pick-like-a-
cre_pi!
-lete him!
cre_pi!
-lete him!
pp

A
piz_zi_ca, l'unghia rin _ tuzzo_la! pizzi _ca, pizzi _ ca, pizzi _ca,
-pick-le him for his men - dac- i - ty! Fret and be - set him for all his cu -
M
piz_zi_ca, l'unghia rin _ tuzzo_la! pizzi _ca, pizzi _ca, pizzi _ca,
-pick-le him for his men - dac -i - ty! Fret and be - set him for all his cu -
Q
piz_zi_ca, l'unghia rin _ tuzzo_la! pizzi _ca,
-pick-le him for his men - dac - i - ty! all his cu -
FAL
ahì! ahì!
Oh! Oh!
piz_zi_ca, l'unghia rin _ tuzzo_la! pizzi _ca, pizzi_ca, pizzi _ ca,
-pick-le him for his men - dac - i - ty! Fret and be - set him for all his cu -
piz_zi_ca, l'unghia rin _ tuzzo_la! pizzi_ca, pizzi_ca, pizzi _ca,
-pick-le him for his men - dac - i - ty! Fret and be - set him for all his cu -
Ch'ei cre_pi di stizza, ch'ei crepi di
To bite him and blight him, to smite and to
Ch'ei cre_pi di stizza, ch'ei crepi di
To bite him and blight him, to smite and to

f
piz-zi-ca, piz-zi-ca, pizzi-ca, l'unghia rin-tuzzo-la! pizzi-ca
-pid-i-ty, Make him re-gret his stu-pen-dous stu-pid-i-ty! Prick him and
f
piz-zi-ca, piz-zi-ca, pizzi-ca, l'unghia rin-tuzzo-la! pizzi-ca
-pid-i-ty, Make him re-gret his stu-pen-dous stu-pid-i-ty! Prick him and
f
piz-zi-ca, piz-zi-ca, pizzi-ca, l'unghia rin-tuzzo-la! pizzi-ca
-pid-i-ty, Make him re-gret his stu-pen-dous stu-pid-i-ty! Prick him and
f
piz-zi-ca, piz-zi-ca, pizzi-ca, l'unghia rin-tuzzo-la! pizzi-ca
-pid-i-ty, Make him re-gret his stu-pen-dous stu-pid-i-ty! Prick him and
f
piz-zi-ca, piz-zi-ca, pizzi-ca, l'unghia rin-tuzzo-la! pizzi-ca
-pid-i-ty, Make him re-gret his stu-pen-dous stu-pid-i-ty! Prick him and
stizza, ch'ei cre-pi di stizza, ch'ei crepi di stizza!
spite him. So pounce on him, hit him, and trounce him and twit him!
stizza, ch'ei cre-pi di stizza, ch'ei crepi di stizza!
spite him. So pounce on him, hit him, and trounce him and twit him!
f
ff

A
piz_zi_ca, piz_zi_ca, piz_zi_ca!
nick him and kick him and tick-le him!
M
piz_zi_ca, piz_zi_ca, piz_zi_ca!
nick him and kick him and tick-le him!
Q
piz_zi_ca, piz_zi_ca, piz_zi_ca!
nick him and kick him and tick-le him!
FAL
piz_zi_ca, piz_zi_ca, piz_zi_ca!
nick him and kick him and tick-le him!
piz_zi_ca, piz_zi_ca, piz_zi_ca!
nick him and kick him and tick-le him!
p
Ruzzo_la, ruzzo_la, ruzzo_la,
Jum-ble and rum-ble and tum-ble and
p
Ruzzo_la, ruzzo_la, ruzzo_la,
Jumble and rumble and tumble and
p

(Ford, Cajus, Pistol and Bardolph lift him up and force him to his knees!)

LO STESSO MOVIMENTO
Dr. C
-tron! Ghiot - ton! Bè -
loon! Buf - foon! Rac -
BAR.
Pol - tron! Pan - cion!
Pol - troon! Bal - loon!
FOR
-tron! Ghiot - ton! Be -
loon! Buf - foon! Rac -
PIS.
Pol - tron! Pan - cion!
Pol - troon! Bal - loon!
LO STESSO MOVIMENTO
(42)
Dr. C
-on! In gi - noc - chion!
-coon! You laughed too soon!
B
Bric - con! In gi - noc - chion!
Ba - boon! You laughed too soon!
FOR
-on! In gi - noc - chion!
-coon! You laughed too soon!
P
Bric - con! In gi - noc - chion!
Ba - boon! You laughed too soon!
ff

ALI.
Guan_cia ri_gon_fia!
Lech - er - ous am - bler!
B
Scon_quas_sa_
Flas - ket a -
FOR
Pan_cia ri_tron_fia!
Treach - er - ous gam - bler!
mf
MEG
Sfon_da se_
Blun - der - ing
QUIC.
Spac_ca far_set_ti!
Bas - ket mis - us - er!
B
_let_ti!
- bus - er!
PIS.
Vuo_ta ba_ri_li!
Won - der con - niv - er!
cres.

M
D'C. - di - li!
div - er!
Sfian - ca giu - men - ti!
Paunch - y rap - scal - lion!
B
Di'
Do
FORD
Tri - pli - ce men - to!
Haunch - y old stal - lion!
P
Di'
Do
f
(Bardolph has taken Quickly's broomstick and is beating Falstaff.)
ALI.
Di' che ti
Do you re -
MEG
Di' che ti
Do you re -
QUIC.
Di' che ti
Do you re -
B
che ti pen -
you re - pent
P
che ti pen -
you re - pent
10

pen - ti!
-pent now?
Di' che ti
Can we re -
pen - ti!
-pent now?
Di' che ti
Can we re -
pen - ti!
-pent now?
Di' che ti
Can we re -
Dr. C.
Uom fro - - do -
Can - we re -
B
- ti.........
now? —
Uom fro - - do -
Can we re-
OR
Uom fro - - do -
Can we re-
P
- ti.........
now? —
Uom fro - - do -
Can we re -
AL
Ahi! ahi! mi pen - to!
I do re - pent now.
ff
mf
10

(*Pistol has taken the stick from Bardolph and is beating Falstaff.*)

(Bardolph takes the stick again and resumes his beating of Falstaff.)

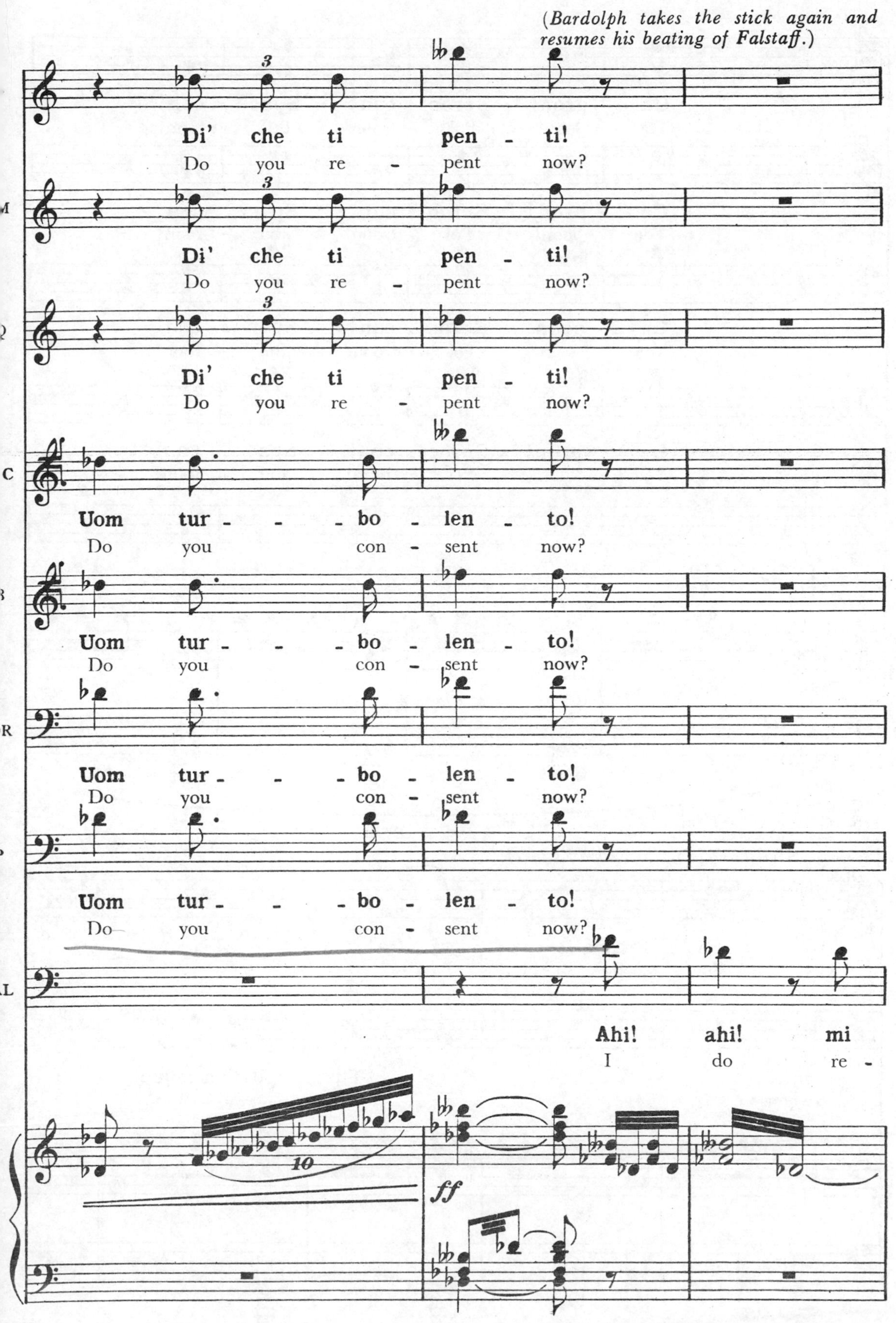
Di' che ti pen - ti!
Do you re - pent now?
Di' che ti pen - ti!
Do you re - pent now?
Di' che ti pen - ti!
Do you re - pent now?
Uom tur - - bo - len - to!
Do you con - sent now?
Uom tur - - bo - len - to!
Do you con - sent now?
Uom tur - - bo - len - to!
Do you con - sent now?
Uom tur - - bo - len - to!
Do you con - sent now?
Ahi! ahi! mi
I do re -
10
ff

D^r C
Ca - pron! Scroc - con! Spac - con!
You loon! Pol - troon! Buf - foon!
B
Ca - pron! Scroc - con! Spac - con!
You loon! Pol - troon! Buf - foon!
FOR
Ca - pron! Scroc - con! Spac - con!
You loon! Pol - troon! Buf - foon!
P
Ca - pron! Scroc - con! Spac - con!
You loon! Pol - troon! Buf - foon!
FAL
pen - to! Per -
-pent now. I
mf
pp
(coming close to Falstaff's face)
B
Ri - for-ma la tua vi - ta!
You keep the Bi - ble hand-y!
FAL
-don! Tu pu-ti d'acqua -
swoon. You ras-cal reek of

ALI.
UN POCO MENO ♩= 100
Do-mi-ne fal-lo ca - sto!
May the Al-might-y fright-en him!
MEG
Do-mi-ne fal-lo ca - sto!
May the Al-might-y fright-en him!
QUIC.
Do-mi-ne fal-lo ca - sto!
May the Al-might-y fright-en him!
Dr C.
Pancia ri - tronfia!
Treach-er-ous gam-bler!
B
Pancia ri - tronfia!
Treach-er-ous gam-bler!
FOR.
Pancia ri - tronfia!
Treach-er-ous gam-bler!
PIS.
Pancia ri - tronfia!
Treach-er-ous gam-bler!
L
-vita!
bran-dy.
Ma sal - vagli l'ad - do-mine.
But nev - er shrink or slight-en him!
THE FAIRIES
p
Pizzica, pizzica,
Prick him and kick him and
UN POCO MENO ♩= 100
pp dolcissimo
(43)

A
Do - mine fal-lo gua - sto!
May the good Lord en-light-en him!
M
Do - mine fal-lo gua - sto!
May the good Lord en-light-en him!
Q
Do - mine fal-lo gua - sto!
May the good Lord en-light-en him!
Dr. C
Pancia ri-tronfia!
Lech-er-ous am-bler!
B
Pancia ri-tronfia!
Lech-er-ous am bler!
FOR
Pancia ri-tronfia!
Lech-er-ous am-bler!
P
Pancia ri-tronfia!
Lech-er-ous am-bler!
FAL
Ma sal - vagli l'ad-do-mine.
But not re-duce or tight-en him!
pizzica!
tick-le him
Pizzica, stuzzica,
and nick him pick like a

A
Fal - lo puni - to Do - mine!
Jus - tice may put her bite on him.
M
Fal - lo puni - to Do - mine!
Jus - tice may put her bite on him.
Q
Fal - lo puni - to Do - mine!
Jus - tice may put her bite on him.
C
Vuota ba - ri - li!
husband re - placer!
B
Vuota ba - ri - li!
husband re - placer!
FOR
Vuota ba - ri - li!
husband re - placer!
P
Vuota ba - ri - li!
husband re - placer!
FAL
Ma sal - vagli l'ad - do - mine.
Good Luck be-stow her might on him!
pizzica!
- pick-le him!
Pizzica, pungi, spil-
Tackle and shackle and

A
Fal - lo penti-to Do - mine!
Heav - en may shed its light on him!
M
Fal - lo penti-to Do - mine!
Heav - en may shed its light on him!
Q
Fal - lo penti-to Do - mine!
Heav - en may shed its light on him!
Dr. C.
Sfianca se - di-li!
virtue dis-gracer
B
Sfianca se - di-li!
virtue dis-gracer
FOR
Sfianca se - di-li!
virtue dis-gracer
P
Sfianca se - di-li!
virtue dis-gracer
FAL
Ma sal - vagli l'ad - do-mine.
And Ve - nus set her sight on him!
-luzzica!
tatter him,
Pizzica, pizzica.
sock him and batter him!

POCO PIÙ ANIMATO ♩=120

C. *ff* Glo - bo d'im-pu - ri - tà! Rispon - - -
Moun - tain of mor - tal sin... your an - - -

B *ff* Glo - bo d'im-pu - ri - tà! Rispon - - -
Moun - tain of mor - tal sin... your an - - -

R *ff* Glo - bo d'im-pu - ri - tà! Rispon - - -
Moun - tain of mor - tal sin... your an - - -

P *ff* Glo - bo d'im-pu - ri - tà! Rispon - - -
Moun - tain of mor - tal sin... your an - - -

3

(44) piz-zi-ca!

POCO PIÙ ANIMATO ♩=120

ff

C. - di. Mon - te di o-be - si -
- swer! Foun - tain of port and

B - di. Mon - te di o-be - si -
- swer! Foun - tain of port and

R - di. Mon - te di o-be - si -
- swer! Foun - tain of port and

P - di. Mon - te di o-be - si -
- swer! Foun - tain of port and

FAL. Ben mi sta.
I a-gree.

pp *ff*

Dr. C
B
FOR
P
FAL
-tà ri-spon - - - - di.
gin . . . your an - - - - swer!
Ben mi sta.
I a-gree.
pp
ff
secca
O-tre di mal-va-si-a rispon - - - di.
Spout of de-ceit and out-rage . . . your an - - - swer!
Co-sì si-a.....
If you say so!
pp

B
Re dei pan-ciu - ti! Re dei cor-nu - ti!
Lout, let me warn— you... I shall un-horn— you!
AL
Va via, tu pu-ti. Va via, tu
You reek of liq-uor... you make me
mf
incalzando a poco a poco sempre
Dr. C.
Fur-fan-te-ri - a! Ga-gliof-fe - ri - a!
Watch how we beat you, How we de - feat you!
B
Fur-fan-te-ri - a! Ga-gliof-fe - ri - a!
Watch how we beat you, How we de - feat you!
FORD
Fur-fan-te-ri - a! Ga-gliof-fe - ri - a!
Watch how we beat you, How we de - feat you!
PIS.
Fur-fan-te-ri - a! Ga-gliof-fe - ri - a!
Watch how we beat you, How we de - feat you!
FAL
pu-ti. Ahi! Co-sì si - a. Ahi! Co-sì
sick-er. Let me en-treat you! Let me en -

Dr C
Fur_fan_te_ri _ a! Gaglioffe _ ri _ a!
Watch how we beat you, How we de_feat you!
(violently)
B
Fur_fan_te_ri _ a! Gaglioffe _ ri _ a! Ed or che il diavo_lo ti por_ti
Watch how we beat you, How we de - feat you! un-til the Dev-il will fi-nal-ly
FOR
Fur_fan_te_ri _ a! Gaglioffe _ ri _ a!
Watch how we beat you, How we de - feat you!
P
Fur_fan_te_ri _ a! Gaglioffe _ ri _ a!
Watch how we beat you, How we de - feat you!
FAL
si_a Ahi! ahi! ahi! ahi!
-treat you! Oh! Oh! Oh! Oh!
B
(His hood slides off his head.)
vi _ _ a!!!
heat - you.
FAL
(rising abruptly)
Nitro! Catrame! Solfo!!! Ri_co_
Thun-der and light-ning! Sa-tan! This is
Più animato
FAL
_no _ sco Bar_dol_ _fo!
Bar - dolph, so help me!
ff

(furiously assaulting Bardolph who retreats)
FAL
Na - so ver - mi - glio! Na - so bar - gi - glio! Pun - tù - ta
Nose like a bun - ion, Nose of a ron - yon, Bump of bi -
p
(45)
le - si - na! Vam - pa di re - si - na! Sa - la - mandra! I - gnis
-bac - i - ty, Lump of sa - lac - i - ty! Sal - a - man - der! Blunt - ed
fa - tu - us! Vecchia ala - barda! Stecca di sar - to - re! Schidion d'in -
bat - tle - ax! Fork of the Dev - il! Mis - er - a - ble mon - grel! In - fer - nal
sempre incalzando e cres:
- fer - no! A ringa secca! Vampi - ro! Ba - si - li - sco! Manigol - do! La -
vi - per! You scum in - car - nate! You bat, you gnat, you rat! You gal - lows - vul - ture! You

FAL
_dro _ ne!
var - let!
Ho det_to. E............ se men _ ti _ sco
I've spok-en. And if I'm ly - ing
ff
p
ALI.
Poco meno
Bra _ vo!
Bra - vo!
MEG
Bra _ vo!
Bra - vo!
QUIC.
Bra _ vo!
Bra - vo!
Dr C.
Bra _ vo!
Bra - vo!
FORD
Bra _ vo!
Bra - vo!
PIS.
Bra _ vo!
Bra - vo!
FAL
Vo_glio che mi si spacchi il cin _ tu _ ro _ ne!!!!
No sin-gle bone of mine shall stay un - brok - en!
(46)
Poco meno
p

Un po_co di pau_sa.-
Let's rest for a mo ment.
m.d.
QUIC.
(aside to Bardolph whom she then draws behind the bushes)
(Vie_ni. Ti co_pri - rò col ve_lo bianco).
(Come, it is time for you to be at - tired.)
FORD
Ed
And
So_no stanco.
I am tired.
or, men_tre vi pas_sa la scal - ma - - na,
now, while we will all en-joy a res - - pite,
p dim.
poco rall:
♩=100
Sir John, di - te:
Sir John, tell me:
♩=100
ppp

MEG
(to Falstaff, sarcastically)
Chi
Say,
FOR
Il cor - nu - - - - to chi è?
Which of us wears the horns?
ALI.
(to Falstaff, sarcastically)
Chi è? Chi è?
Yes, who? Yes, who?
M
è? Chi è?
who! Say, who!
allarg. un poco e
(taking off her mask)
A
Vi sie - te fat - to mu - to?
You seem con - fused and shak - en.
dim.

(interrupting him)
Sba - glia - te nel sa -
I fear, you are mis -
(reaching for Ford's hand)
Ca - - ro Si - gnor Fon - ta - na...
Good Mas-ter Brook, I greet you . .
(47)
- lu - to. Quest'è Ford mio ma - ri - - - -
- tak - en . . . This is Ford, my good hus - - - -
pp
LO STESSO MOVIMENTO = 100
- to.
QUIC. band.
Ca - va - lie -
I am hon -
FAL.
LO STESSO MOVIMENTO = 100
Re - ve -
I am

allarg.
a tempo
leggero
Q
- - - rò, Voi cre - de - ste due don - ne co - si
- allarg. - ored! So you fan - cied two la - dies, choos - ing
FAL
- ren - - - - za.
hon - - - - ored!
pp
allarg.
a tempo
pp
marcato
Q
grul - le, Così ci - trulle, Da dar - si anima e cor - po al -
free - ly, could be so sil - ly and court, bod - y and soul, their
Q
- l'Av - ver - sie - ro, Per un uom vec - chio, sù - dicio ed o -
own per - di - tion for some old charm - er clear - ly out of

ALI.
E con quel pe - so!
cloud-ed his rea - son?
MEG
Con quella te - sta cal - va... E con quel pe - so!
... whose van - i - ty and fat have cloud-ed his rea - son?
- be - so... Con quella te - sta cal - va... E con quel pe - so!
sea - son whose van - i - ty and fat have cloud-ed his rea - son?
(48)
FOR.
Par - lan chia - ro.
Now you know it!
cres.
L
In - co - min - cio ad ac - cor - - ger - mi d'es - ser
I be - gin to per - ceive that like - ly I

ALI.

Un cer - vo
A roe - buck!

FOR.

Un
A

FAL

stato un so - ma - - - ro.
shall have been made an ass.

A

Ah! ah!
Ha, ha!

MEG

Ah! ah!
Ha, ha!

Un
A

QUIC.

Ah! ah!
Ha, ha!

FOR

bu - e e un mo - - stro raro, un mostro
bull - ock! a cu - - rious mon-ster, a fun-ny

PIS.

Ah! ah!
Ha, ha!

CHORUS

WOMEN

Ah! ah!
Ha, ha!

TENORS

Ah! ah!
Ha ha!

BASSES

Ah! ah!
Ha ha!

un bu - e, un cer - vo, un bu - e, un
A bull - ock! A roe - buck! A bull - ock! A
cer - vo, un cer - vo, un bu - e, un
roe - buck! A roe - buck! A bull - ock! A
Un mostro ra - - - - -
A fun-ny freak!
ra - - - - - - - -
freak!
Un mostro ra - - - -
A fun-ny freak!
Un mostro ra - -
A fun-ny freak!
Un mostro
A fun-ny
cres.
f

(long silence)
A
bu - - e, ah! ah! ah! ah! ah! ah!
roe - - buck! Ha, ha, ha, ha, ha, ha!
M
bu - - e, ah! ah! ah! ah! ah! ah!
roe - - buck! Ha, ha, ha, ha, ha, ha!
Q
- - - ro, ah! ah! ah! ah! ah! ah!
Ha, ha, ha, ha, ha, ha!
FOR
- - - ro, ah! ah! ah! ah! ah! ah!
Ha, ha, ha, ha, ha, ha!
P
- - - ro, ah! ah! ah! ah! ah! ah!
Ha, ha, ha, ha, ha, ha!
Un mostro ra - ro, ah! ah! ah! ah! ah! ah!
A funny freak! Ha, ha, ha, ha, ha, ha!
- - - ro, ah! ah! ah! ah! ah! ah!
Ha, ha, ha, ha, ha, ha!
ra - - ro, ah! ah! ah! ah! ah! ah!
freak! Ha, ha, ha, ha, ha, ha!
ff
(long silence)

MODERATO ♩ = 80
FAL. (having regained his composure)
Ogni sorta di gente dozzi _ na _ le Mi beffa e se ne
Thus a rabble of com-mon place barbar - i - - ans de-rides me, Gloat-ing in
MODERATO ♩ = 80
(49)
p
glo _ ria; Pur, senza me co _ stor con tanta boria Non a _
glo - ry! Yet, but for me, this dull and wit-less sto-ry Would not
f
pp
leggero
_ vrebbe _ ro un briccio _ lo di sa _ le. Son
e-ven have a pinch of salt to spice it! 'Tis
pp
p
LO STESSO MOVIMENTO ♩ = 80
cres.
io, son io, son io, che vi fa scaltri.
I, yes, I a - lone, no-ble and clev-er,
LO STESSO MOVIMENTO ♩ = 80
f
p
pp

dolce
FAL
L'ar-gu-zia mi-a cre-a l'ar-guzia degl'al-
Whose gay ad-ven-ture you will re-mem-ber for-ev-
leggero
pp
ALI.
Ma bra-vo!
Well spok-en!
MEG
Ma bra-vo!
Well spok-en!
QUIC.
Ma bra-vo!
Well spok-en!
FORD
Per gli Dei! Se non ridessi ti sconquas-se-rei!
Be it said that, had I not had fun, you would be dead!
FAL
TENORS -tri.
-er!
CHORUS
Ma bra-vo!
Well spok-en!
BASSES
Ma bra-vo!
Well spok-en! ANIMATO
(50)
f

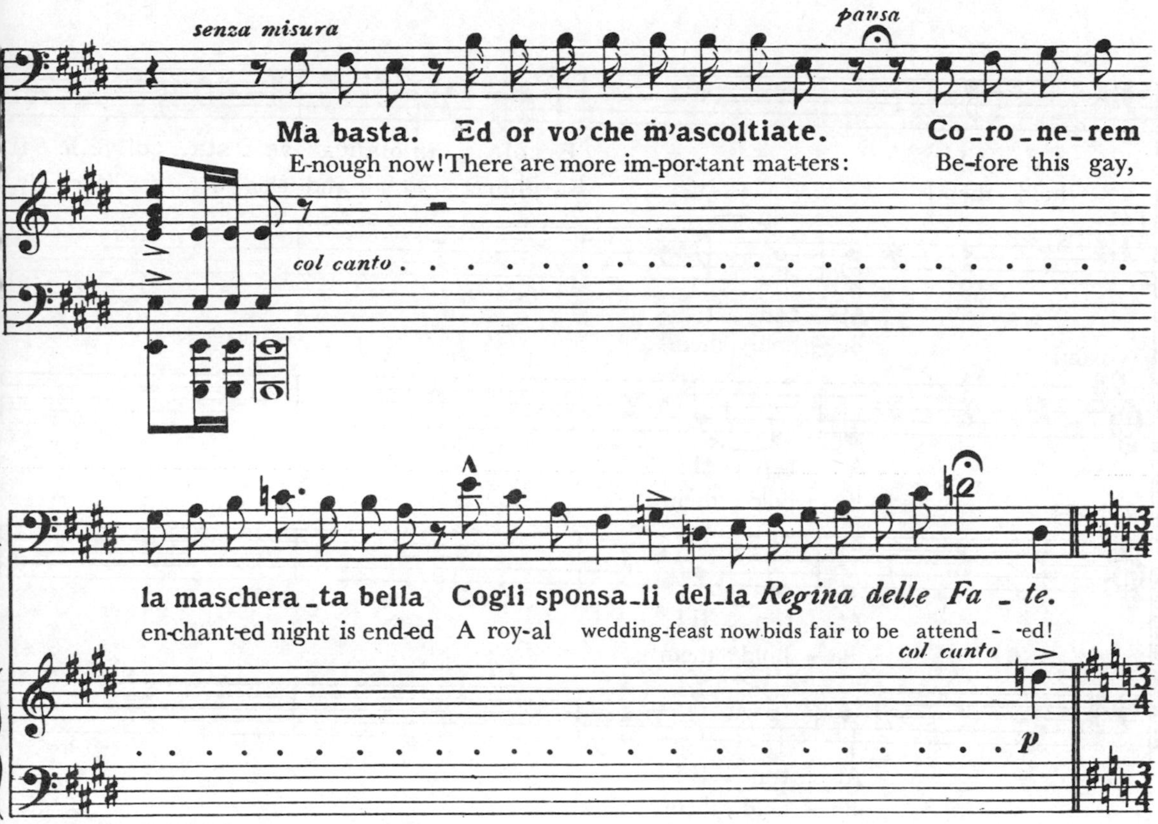

senza misura
pausa
Ma basta. Ed or vo' che m'ascoltiate. Co_ro_ne_rem
E-nough now! There are more im-por-tant mat-ters: Be-fore this gay,
col canto
la maschera_ta bella Cogli sponsa_li del_la Regina delle Fa_te.
en-chant-ed night is end-ed A roy-al wedding-feast now bids fair to be attend - -ed!
col canto
p

(Dr. Cajus and Bardolph, disguised as Queen of the Fairies, advance slowly, holding hands. Bardolph's face is hidden by his veil while Dr. Cajus wears a mask.)

ALLEGRETTO ♩ = 88
dolce
p
FORD
Già s'a-vanza il cor - teg - gio nu - zï - a - le. È
See the cou-ple ap - proach - ing from the dis - tance. Be

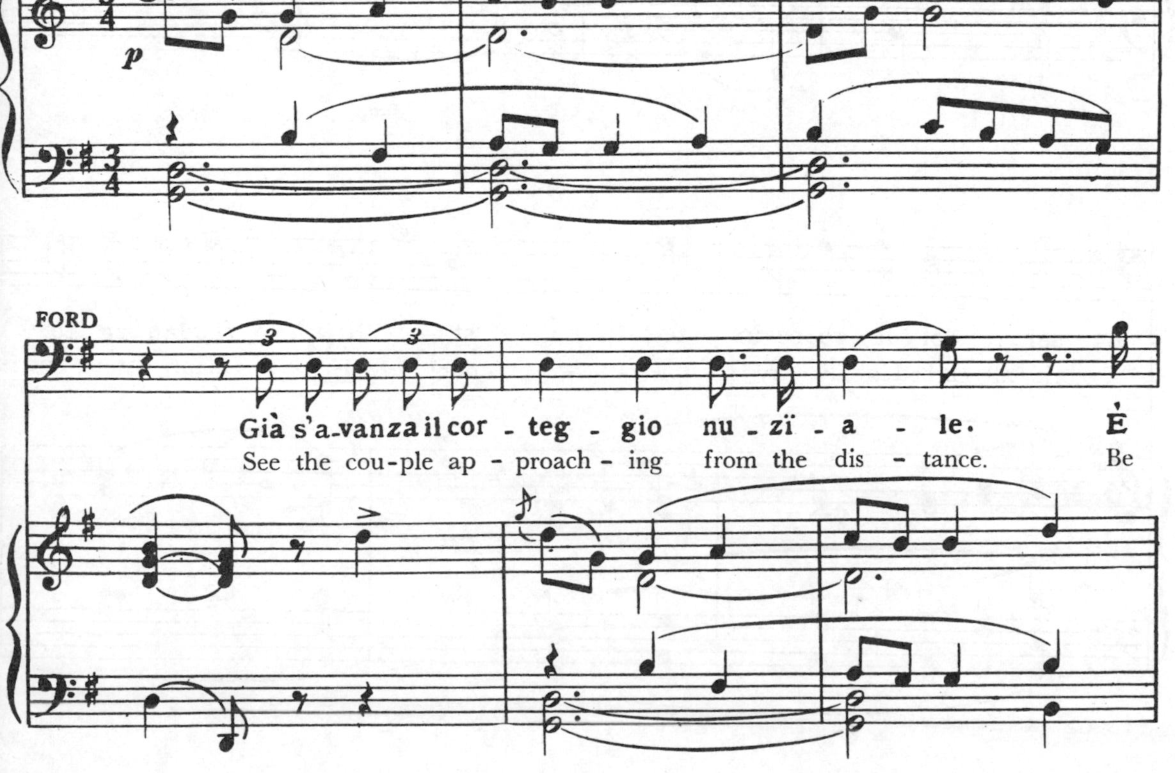

FOR
des - sa!
-hold them!
Eccola in bianca ve - sta, col ve-lo e il
Ravishing, so fair and slen - der, The love - ly
FAL.
At - ten - ti!
Be - hold them!
WOMEN
A - ten - ti!
Be - hold them!
TENORS
At - ten - ti!
Be - hold them!
BASSES
At - ten - ti!
Be - hold them!
dolcissimo
FOR
ser-to del-le ro-se in te - - - sta E il fi-dan-za-to
bride all garbed in silv-'ry splen - - - dor! He, manly, strong and
pp

(*Bardolph and Dr. Cajus arrive center-stage, surrounded by Fairies.*)

su - o ch'io le di - spo - si. Cir-conda-te-la o
hand - some, cho-sen with my as - sist-ance. Let the spir-its sur-
(51)
Nin - fe!
-round them.
(*presenting Ann and Fenton. Ann is covered by a long blue veil, Fenton still wears his monk's robe.*)
ALICE
Un'al - tra coppia d'a-manti de-sï-
An-oth - er pair of young hearts in sweet com-
-o - si Chie - de d'esser am - mes - sa agli augu-
-mun - ion Came here, fer-vent-ly hop - ing that you would

forward, carrying lanterns. The smallest one, carried by Alice, holds his tiny lantern on a level with

Bardolph's face. Ann and Fenton, hand in hand, are standing slightly off center-stage.)

apotheosis: a deification or glorification

(As soon as they hear Ford's command, Cajus and Fenton drop their masks. Ann unveils her face, and Quickly pulls the hood off Bardolph's head. All the faces are uncovered.)

(52) VIVACE ♩=120

R
Giù le maschere e i ve_li. A_po_te _ ò _ _ si!
Now re-move your dis-guis-es! A-poth-e - o - sis!

cres. f VIVACE ff

ALI.
Ah! ah! ah! ah!
Ha, ha, ha, ha!

MEG
Ah! ah! ah! ah!
Ha, ha, ha, ha!

QUIC.
Ah! ah! ah! ah!
Ha, ha, ha, ha!

DC.
(recognizing Bardolph)
Spa _ ven_to!
Oh ter-ror!

FAL.
Ah! ah! ah! ah!
Ha, ha, ha, ha!

FOR.
(thunderstruck)
Tradi_
What an

PIS.
Ah! ah! ah! ah!
Ha, ha, ha, ha!

WOMEN
Ah! ah! ah! ah!
Ha, ha, ha, ha!

TENORS
Ah! ah! ah! ah!
Ha, ha, ha, ha!

BASSES
Ah! ah! ah! ah!
Ha, ha, ha, ha!

ff

A
M
Q
Dr C
(petrified)
Ho spo_
I am
FAL
A_po_te_ò - - - si!
A-poth-e - o - - - sis!
(noticing the other couple)
FOR
_mento!
er-ror!
Fenton con mia figlia!!!
Fen-ton with my daugh-ter!
P
A_po_te_ò - - - si!
A-poth-e - o - - - sis!
A_po_te_ò - - - si!
A-poth-e - o - - - sis!
A_po_te_ò - - - si!
A-poth-e - o - - - sis!
A_po_te_ò - - - si!
A-poth-e - o - - - sis!
ff

Ah! Ah! Vit _ toria! Ev _ vi _ va! Ev _
Ha, ha! We tri-umph! Be hap-py! Be
Ah! Ah! Vit _ toria! Ev _ vi _ va! Ev _
Ha, ha! We tri-umph! Be hap-py! Be
Ah! Ah! Vit _ toria! Ev _ vi _ va! Ev _
Ha, ha! We tri-umph! Be hap-py! Be
marcato
_ sa _ to Bar _ dolfo!! Spa _ ven _ to! Spa _
mar- ried to Bar-dolph! Oh ter - ror! Oh
Ah! Ah! Ev _ vi _ va! Ev _
Ah! Ah! Be hap-py! Be
Ah! Ah! Ev _ vi _ va! Ev _
Ha, ha! Be hap-py! Be
Ah! Ah! Ev _ vi _ va! Ev _
Ha, ha! Be hap-py! Be
Ah! Ah! Ev _ vi _ va! Ev _
Ha, ha! Be hap-py! Be
Ah! Ah! Ev _ vi _ va! Ev _
Ha, ha! Be hap-py! Be

(stepping to Ford)
A
_vi _va!
hap-py!
M
_vi _va!
hap-py!
Q
_vi _va!
hap-py!
D!C
_vento!
ter-ror!
FAL
_vi _va!
hap-py!
(still in a state of shock)
FOR
Oh! mera _viglia!!
I can-not grasp it!
P
_vi _va!
hap-py!
_vi _va!
hap-py!
_vi _va!
hap-py!
_vi _va!
hap-py!
p rall. a poco a poco fino al..

♩ = 100
ALI.
grazioso (a Ford)
L'uom ca_de spesso nel_le re_ti or_di_te........ Dal - le...
The fin-est web our per-fi - dy_ can_fash-ion ___ will of -
♩ = 100
...... pp
allarg.
.... ma_li_zie su - e.
- ten_trap the weav - er!
(walking up to Ford and bowing, with irony)
FAL.
Ca - - ro buon Mes_ser
Ah, ___ my good Mas - ter
(53)
p
Ford, ed o - ra, di - te: Lo scor_
Ford, I pray you tell me which of

Dr. C.
(pointing to Ford)
Tu.
You.
FORD
(pointing to Dr. Cajus)
Lui.
He.
No.
No.
FAL.
-na - - to chi è?
us is the fool!
Più animato
p
ALI.
(pointing to Falstaff, Ford and Dr. Cajus)
No!
No!
Tut-ti e
There are
FEN.
(indicating both Ford and Dr. Cajus)
Lor.
Both.
(stepping close to Ford)
Dr. C
Sì.
Yes.
Noi.
We.
BAR.
(indicating both Ford and Dr. Cajus)
Voi.
You.
FAL
Tut - ti e du-e!
There are two now!
f
p

COME PRIMA ♩=88
A
tre!
three!
COME PRIMA ♩=88
(54) mf
(to Ford, referring to Ann and Fenton)
Vol - - gi - ti e mi - ra quel - l'an - sie leg -
Look on the chil - dren on pins and on
dim.
- gia dre.
nee - dles!
NAN.
(entreating Ford with hands folded)
Per - do - na - - te - ci o pa - dre.
Dear - est Fath - - er, for - give us!
dim. sempre

FORD
Chi schi_va_re non può la pro_pria
When you suf-fer de - feat, don't let it
dim.

FOR
no _ ja L'accet _ ti di buon gra _ do.
blight you: It nev-er shall dis - grace you!
dim.
morendo

ALLEGRO MOSSO
FOR
Fac _ cia _ mo il pa_ren _ ta _ do E che il
My chil - dren, I em - brace you! Let me
ALLEGRO MOSSO

ALI.
Ev - vi - - - va!
Be hap - - - py!
NAN.
Ev - vi - - - va!
Be hap - - - py!
MEG
Ev - vi - - - va!
Be hap - - - py!
QUI.
Ev - vi - - - va!
Be hap - - - py!
FEN.
Ev - vi - - - va!
Be hap - - - py!
BAR.
Ev - vi - - - va!
Be hap - - - py!
PIS.
Ev - vi - - - va!
Be hap - - - py!
FOR
ciel vi dia gio - ia.
bless and u-nite you!
FAL.
Un
A
ff
FOR
Poi con Sir Fal-staff, tutti, andiamo a
Then with Sir John I ask you all to
FAL
co - ro e terminiam la sce - na.
rous - ing trib-ute to the win - ner!
ff

A
Ev_vi _ va!
We thank you!
N
Ev_vi _ va!
We thank you!
M
Ev_vi _ va!
We thank you!
Q
Ev_vi _ va!
We thank you!
FEN
Ev_vi _ va!
We thank you!
Dr C
Ev_vi _ va!
We thank you!
B
Ev_vi _ va!
We thank you!
P
Ev_vi _ va!
We thank you!
FOR
ce _ _ na!
din _ _ ner.
FAL
Ev_vi _ va!
We thank you!
WOMEN
Ev_vi _ va!
We thank you!
TENORS
Ev_vi _ va!
We thank you!
BASSES
Ev_vi _ va!
We thank you!
CHORUS
(55)
ff
poco allarg:

ALICE ALL° BRIOSO ♩= 120

QUICKLY

FENTON

FALSTAFF

Tutto nel mondo è burla. L'uom......... è na_to burlo_ne, bur_lo_ne, bur-

Let us en-joy our fol-ly! Man is born to be jol-ly for-ev-er and

NANNETTA

MEG

Dr. CAJUS

FORD

BARDOLFO

PISTOLA

CHORUS

SOPRANOS

ALTOS

TENORS

BASSES

ALL° BRIOSO ♩= 120

A
Q
FEN
Tutto nel mon_do è burla. L'uom................................ è nato burlone, burlone, bur_
Let us en-joy our fol-ly! Man is born to be jol-ly for-ev-er and
FAL
_lone, tut _ to è bur _ la, l'uom è nato burlo _ ne, è nato burlone, burlone, bur_
ev-er. All is fol - ly. Man is born to be jol-ly, is born to be jol-ly for-ev-er and
N
M
Dr C
FOR
B
P

Tut-to nel mon-do è bur-la. L'uom
Let us en-joy our fol-ly! Man
-lo-ne, tut-to è bur-la, l'uom è na-to bur-lo-
ev-er. All is fol-ly. Man is born to be jol-
-lo-ne, tut-to è bur-la, l'uom è na-
ev-er. All is fol-ly. Man is jol-

A
Tut_to nel mon _ do è
Let us en - joy our
Q
pp
.... è na_to bur_lo_ne, bur_lo_ne, bur - lo_ne, tut - - to è bur -
is born to be jol-ly for ev-er and ev-er. All is fol -
FEN
pp
_ne, è na_to bur_lo_ne, bur_lo_ne, bur - lo_ne, tut - to è burla nel mon -
-ly, is born to be jol-ly for ev-er and ev-er. Let us laugh at our fol -
FAL
pp
_to è na_to bur_lo_ne, bur_lo_ne, bur - lo_ne, l'uom è na - _to bur_
-ly, is born to be jol-ly for ev-er and ev-er. Man is born to be
N
M
Dr. C
FOR
B
P
pp

A
Q
EN
AL
N
M
D.r C
FOR
B
P
f
pp
bur - la. L'uom è na-to bur-lo-ne, bur-lo-ne, bur-
fol - ly! Man is born to be jol-ly for ev - er and
la. L'uom è na-to burlo - ne, è na-to bur-lo-ne, bur-lo-ne, bur-
ly! Man is born to be jol - ly, is born to be jol-ly for ev-er and
- do. L'uom è na - - - to, è na-to bur-lo-ne, bur-lo-ne, bur-
ly! Man is jol - - - ly, is born to be jol-ly for ev-er and
- lo - - - - ne, è na-to bur-lo-ne, bur-lo-ne, bur-
jol - - - - ly, is born to be jol-ly for ev-er and

A
lo - ne.
ev - er.
Q
lo - ne.
ev - er.
FEN
lo - ne. Nel suo cer - vel
ev - er. His vain de - fens
FAL
lo - ne. Nel su - o cer - vel - lo ciur - la sem
ev - er. His i - dle pre - tens - es, vain de - fens
N
Tut - to nel mon - do è
Let us en - joy our
M
Tut - to nel mon - do è bur - la, tut - to è bur
Let us en - joy our fol - ly! All is fol
D.r C
FOR
B
Tut - to, tut - to nel mon - do è
Fol - ly! Let us en - joy our
P
Tut - to, tut - to nel mon - do tut - to è bur
Let us en - joy our fol - ly! Yes, our fol
(56)
p stacc.

Nel suo cer_vel_lo ciur_la sem_pre,
All his pre-tens-es, be-fud-dle his sens - es.
Nel suo cer_vel_lo ciur_la sem - pre................ la sua ra-
All his pre-tens-es, be-fud-dle his sens - es con-found his
-lo ciur - la sem - pre la sua ra-
-es, his in - ane pre - tens-
-pre, ciur_la sem_pre sem_pre................ la sua ragio -
-es and im-ag-ined of-fens - es Trou-ble his sens -
bur - la, tut - to è bur - la.
fol - ly, en-joy our fol - ly!
-la.
-ly!
Tut_to nel mon - do è
Let us en-joy our.
Tut_to nel mon - do è bur_la, tut - to è bur-
Let us en-joy our fol - ly! Yes, our fol-
bur - la. L'uom è na - to bur_lo -
fol - ly! Man is born to be jol -
-la. L'uom è na_to bur_lo - ne................ na_to bur_lo -
-ly! Man is born to be jol - ly, born to be jol -
N
L
M
C
OR
B
P

A
sem - pre.............. la sua.............. ra-gio -
They haunt and taunt his fool -
Q
gion, sem - pre, sem - pre, la sua ra-gio -
mind. They haunt and taunt his fool - ish
FEN
gion, sem - pre, sem - pre, la sua ra-gio -
-es, They haunt and taunt his fool - ish
FAL
ne, sem - pre, sem - pre, sem-pre, sempre la sua ra -
-es, They haunt and taunt and con-found his fool - ish
N
L'uom............ è na - to bur-lo -
Man is born, is born to be jol -
M
L'uom è na - to. è na-to bur-lo -
Man is born, yes, man is born to be jol -
Dr. C
bur - la. L'uom è na - to, è na-to bur-lo -
fol - ly! Man is born, yes, man is born to be jol -
FOR
la, l'uom è na - to, na - to, l'uom è na-to bur lo -
ly! Man is jol - ly! Yes, man, man is born to be jol -
B
ne l'uom è na - to, è na-to bur-lo -
ly, Man is born, yes, man is born to be jol -
P
ne, l'uom è na - to, na - to, l'uom è na-to bur-lo -
ly! Man is jol - ly! Yes, man, man is born to be jol -
Tut - to nel mon - do, nel mon - do è bur -
Man is born, is born to be jol -
Tut - to, tut - to, nel mon-do è bur -
Man is born, yes man is born to be jol -
Tut - to, tut - to, nel mon-do è bur -
They haunt and taunt his fool - ish
L'uom è na - to, na - to, l'uom è na-to bur-lo -
Man is jol - ly! Yes, man, man is born to be jol -

ne.
ish mind.

ne, la sua ra-gion.
mind, his fool-ish mind.

ne.
mind.

gion.
mind.

ne. L'uom è na-to bur-lo
ly! Man is born to be jol-ly!

ne. L'uom è na-to bur-
ly! Man is born to be

ne.
ly!

ne.
ly!

ne.
ly!

la.
ly!

la.
ly!

la.
mind

ne.
ly!

(57)

A
Q
pp e stacc.
Tut-to nel mon-do è burla, nel mon-do è bur - - - - - - -
Let us en-joy — our fol-ly, en-joy — our fol - - - - - - -
FEN
pp
L'uom è na-to bur-lo - ne, è nato bur-lo-ne, bur-lo - -
Man is born to be jol - ly! Yes, he is born — to be — a
FAL
pp
Tut-to nel mon - do è bur-la, è bur - - - - -
Let us en-joy our fol-ly! Man's a
N
- ne
Yes!
M
- lo - ne.
jol - ly!
Dr. C
FOR
B
P
pp e stacc.

pp e stacc.

A

Tut_to nel mon_do è burla, nel mon_do è bur - - - - - - - -
Let us en - joy — our fol-ly, en - joy — our fol - - - - - - -

Q

- la, l'uom è na_to bur - lo - ne, è na_to bur_lo_ne, bur_lo -
- ly! Man is born to be jol - ly, Yes, he is born — to be_a

EN

- ne, tut_to nel mon - do è bur_la, è bur - - - -
fool! Let us en - joy our fol - ly, fol - - - -

AL

- la.
fool!

N

M

D.r C

FOR

B

P

A
Q
FEN
FAL
N
M
Dr. C
FOR
B
P
-la
-ly!
-ne,
fool!
tut-to nel mon - do è
Let us en - joy our
-la
-ly!
tut - - to è bur -
All is fol -
Tut-ti gabba - ti,tut-ti gab - ba - ti,tut - - - - - - -
Lean-er or fat - ter, what does it mat - ter, let us
Tut-ti gabba - ti,tut-ti gab - ba - ti,tut - - - - - - -
Lean-er or fat - ter,what does it mat - ter, let us
Tut-ti gabba - ti,tut-ti gab - ba - ti,tut - - - - - - -
Lean-er or fat - ter,what does it mat - ter, let us
Tut - - - - - - ti gab-
What does it
pp
Tut-ti, tut-ti gab-
Man is born to be
pp
Tutti, tut-ti gab-ba - - - - -
Man-is-born-to-be-jol -
pp
Tut - - - - - - ti gab-
pp What does it
Tut - - - - - - ti gab-
pp What does it
Tut - - - - - - ti gab-
pp What does it
Tut - - - - - - ti gab-
What does it
(58)
mf

tut_to nel mon _ do è
Let us en_joy our
bur _ la,
fol _ ly!
_la
tut _ _ _ to è bur _ _
_ly!
All _ is fol _ _
_ti, tut_ti gabba _ ti, tut_ti gab _ ba _ ti, tut _ _ _ _ _
laugh. I_dly we chat_ter frol_ic and flat _ ter, let us
_ti, tut_ti gabba _ ti, tut_ti gab _ ba _ ti, tut _ _ _ _ _
laugh. I_dly we chat_ter, frol_ic and flat _ ter, let us
_ti, tut_ti gabba _ ti, tut_ti gab _ ba _ ti, tut _ _ _ _ _
laugh. I_dly we chat_ter, frol_ic and flat _ ter, let us
_ba_ti, tut _ _ _ _ _ ti gab_
mat_ter, What does it
_ba_ti, tut_ti tut_ti gab_
jol_ly! Let us laugh at our
_ti tut_ti tut_ti gabba _ _ _ _
_ly! Let us laugh at our fol _ _ _ _
_ba_ti, tut _ _ _ _ _ ti gab_
matter, What does it
_ba_ti, tut _ _ _ _ _ ti gab_
mat_ter, What does it
_ba_ti, tut _ _ _ _ _ ti gab_
matter, What does it
_ba_ti, tut _ _ _ _ _ ti gab_
mat_ter, What does it

A
bur - la, tut - to è bur - la,
-fol - ly, All - is - fol - ly,
Q
tut-ti gabba
I-dly we chat-
FEN
-la, tut-ti gabba - ti, tut-ti gab-
-ly! I-dly we chat- - ter, what does it
FAL
Tut-ti gabba - ti, tut-ti gab - ba - ti! Irri-de l'un l'al - tro ogni mor-
I - dly we chat - ter, frol-ic and flat - ter, Lean-er or fat - ter, what does it
N
-ti!
laugh!
M
ti!
laugh!
Dr C
-ti!
laugh!
FOR
-ba-ti!
mat-ter!
B
-ba-ti!
fol-ly!
P
-ti!
-ly!
-ba-ti!
matter!
-ba-ti!
mat-ter!
-ba-ti!
mat-ter!
-ba-ti!
mat ter!

tut-ti gabba - - ti! Ma ri-de ben, ri-de ben chi
I-dly we chat - - - ter! Fun is the tri-umph of mind o-ver
-ti!
-ter!
Ma ri-de ben, ri-de ben chi
Fun is the tri-umph of mind o-ver
-ba - ti!
mat - ter!
Ma ri-de ben chi
Triumph of mind o-ver
-tal, ir-ri-de l'un l'al - tro ogni mor-tal, Ma ri-de ben, ri-de ben chi
mat - ter. Let us be mer-ry and let us pre - tend: Fun is the tri-umph of mind o-ver

A
ri - de la ri - sa - ta fi - nal.
mat - ter If you laugh in the - end!
Q
ri - de la ri - sa - ta fi - nal.
mat - ter If you laugh in the end!
FEN
ri - de la ri - sa - ta fi - nal.
mat - ter If you laugh in the end!
FAL
ri - de la ri - sa - ta fi - nal.
mat - ter If we laugh in the end!
N
pp
Ma ri - de ben, ri - de ben, ri - de ben chi
Lean - er or fat - ter, we frol - ic and flat - ter and
M
pp
Ma ri - de ben, ri - de ben, ri - de ben chi
Lean - er or fat - ter, we frol - ic and flat - ter and
Dr. C
pp
Tut - to nel mon - do è
Let - us - en - joy our
FOR
B
pp
tut - ti, tut - ti gab - ba - ti, gabba - ti!
Let us laugh at our fol - ly, en - joy it,
P
pp
tut - ti, tut - ti gab - ba - ti, tut - ti gab -
Let us laugh at our fol - ly, won - der ful
pp
tut - ti gab -
wonderful
pp
tut - ti gab -
won - der - ful
pp
tut - ti, tut - ti gab - ba - ti, gabba - ti!
Let us laugh at our fol - ly, en - joy it,
pp
tut - ti, tut - ti gab - ba - ti, tut - ti gab -
Let us laugh at our fol - ly, won - der - ful
(59)
pp
pp

pp
Ma ri_de ben,ri_de ben,ri_de ben chi ri - de
Lean-er or fat-ter we frol-ic and flat-ter and chat - ter.
pp
Ma ri_de ben,ri_de ben,ri_de ben chi ri - de
Lean-er or fat-ter we frol-ic and flat-ter and chat - ter.
N
pp
Tut_to nel mon - do è burla,
Let us en - joy our fol-ly!
L
Ir - ri -
My friends,
N
ri_de
chat ter.
pp
ma ri_de ben,ri_de ben chi
Fun is the tri-umph of mind o-ver
M
pp
ri_de
chat-ter.
ma ri_de ben,ri_de ben chi
Fun is the tri-umph of mind o-ver
C
burla.
fol-ly.
OR
B
gabba - ti!
en-joy it!
P
- ba - ti, tut_ti gab - ba - ti!
fol - ly, won-der-ful fol - ly!
- ba - ti, tut_ti gab - ba - ti!
fol - ly, won-der-ful fol - ly!
- ba - ti, tut_ti gab - ba - ti!
fol - ly, won-der-ful fol - ly!
gabba - ti!
en-joy it!
- ba - ti, tut_ti gab - ba - ti!
fol - ly, won-der-ful fol - ly!

A
ma ri de ben
Laugh-ter is all
Q
ma........... ri-de ben chi ri-de
Laugh - ter is all that mat-ters.
FEN
ma........... ri-de ben chi ri-de
Laugh - ter is all that mat-ters.
FAL
- de ir-ri-de l'un l'al - tro o-gni mor tal,
Oh! Let us be mer-ry and let us pre-tend:
N
ri - de...
mat- - ter.
M
ri - de...
mat- - ter.
tut-to nel mon - do è
Let us en-joy our
Dr.C
Ma ri - de
Fun is — the
FOR
Ma ri-de ben, ri-de ben, ri-de ben chi
Let us be mer-ry and let us for ev-er pre-
B
P

chi
that
ri - de
mat - ters.
ma ri - de ben, ri - de ben chi ri - de
Fun is the tri-umph of mind o-ver mat - ter.
ma ri - de ben chi
Fol-ly is all that
ma ri - de ben, ri - de ben, ri - de ben chi
Lean-er or fat-ter, we frol-ic and flat-ter and
bur - la, l'uom l'uom è na - to bur - lo - ne, bur - lo - ne, bur -
fol - ly! Man, man is born to be jol - ly for ev-er and
ben, ma ri - de ben, ri - de ben chi ri - de la ri - sa - ta fi -
tri - umph of mind o-ver mat - ter If you, if you laugh in the
ri - de la ri - sa - ta fi - nal,
-tend! What do you lose if you laugh in the end?

A: la – ri – sa – ta fi – nal,
If — you laugh — in — the end.

Q: la – ri – sa – ta fi – nal. ah! ah!
If — you laugh — in the end. Ah! Ah!

FEN: la – ri – sa – ta fi – nal.
If — you laugh — in the end.

FAL: ri – de la – ri – sa – ta fi – nal.
mat – ters If — we laugh — in — the end.

N: ri – de ma ri – de ben chi ri – – –
chat – ter. But — what does — it mat – ter,

M: lo – ne ah!
ev – er. Ha!

D^r^C: – nal .... Tut – ti gabba – – –
end ——— What does it mat – – –

FOR: ma ri – de
Let us pre –

B: tut – – – – – – –
What

P: tut – – – – – – –
What

tut – – – – – – –
What

tut – – – – – – –
What

ma ri_de ben chi ri - - de
Yes, what does it mat - - ter

ah! ah! ah! ah!
Ha! Ha! Ha! Ha!

Tut_ti gabba - - - ti!
What does it mat - - - ter?

_de la ri_sa ta fi -
what? If you laugh in the

ah! ah! ah! ah!
Ha! Ha! Ha! Ha!

_ti, tut_ti gab_ba - - - -
-ter, What does it mat - - -

ben ma ri_de ben .... ri_de ben chi
-tend, Let us pre - tend, what does it

_ti gab _ ba - - - - - -
does it mat - - - - - -

_ti gab _ ba - - - - - -
does it mat - - - - - -

_ti gab _ ba - - - - - -
does it mat - - - - - -

_ti gab _ ba - - - - - -
does it mat - - - - - -

A
la ri-sa - ta fi - nal, tut-to nel mon - - -
if you laugh in the end? Let us en-joy
Q
ah! ah! Tut-to nel mon-do è bur - -
Ha! Ha! Let us en-joy our fol - -
FEN
Tut-ti gabba - - - - ti! Tut - - to nel mon-do è
What does it mat - - - - ter? Let us en - joy our
FAL
Tut-to nel mon - do è
Let us en-joy our
N
- nal.
end.
M
ah! ah! ah!
Ha! Ha! Ha!
Dr. C
- ti!
- ter?
FOR
ri - de............ la ri-sa-ta fi - nal.
mat - ter if we laugh in the end?
B
ti!
ter?
P
ti!
ter?
ti!
ter?
ti!
ter?

- - - - - - do è bur_la,
our fol - ly!

_la, tut_to nel mon do è bur_la, l'uom ....
_ly! Let us en - joy our fol - ly! Man,

bur_la, tut _ to, tut_to nel mon_do è bur_la.
fol - ly! Laugh and let us en - joy — our fol - ly!

bur_la, tut _ to, tut_to nel mon_do è bur - la, è bur - la.
fol - ly! Laugh and let us en - joy — our fol - ly, our fol - ly!

Tut_to nel mon - - -
Let us en - joy

Tut_to nel mon_do è bur -
Let us en - joy — our fol -

Tut - - to nel mon_do è
Let us en - joy our

Tut_to nel mon - do è
Let us en - joy our

L'uom ....
Let

A
Q
FEN
FAL
N
M
Dr C
FOR
B
P
pp
tut_ti gab_ba_
What does it mat-
..... l'uom è na_to bur_lo - ne: tut -
Man is born to be jol - ly! You
L'uom è na_to bur_lo - ne
Man_ is born to be jol - ly!
L'uom è na_to bur_lo - ne
Man_ is born to be jol - ly!
do è bur_la,
our fol - ly!
_la, tut_to nel mon - do è bur_la,
_ly, Let us en_joy our fol - ly!
bur_la tut - to, tut_to nel mon_do è bur_la,
fol - ly! Let us en_joy_ en_joy our fol - ly!
bur - la tut - to, tut_to nel mon_do è bur_la,
fol - ly! Let us en-joy, en-joy our fol - ly!
f
tut - to, tut_to nel mon_do è bur_la,
Let us en-joy, en - joy our fol - ly!
tut - to, tut_to nel mon_do è bur_la,
Let us en-joy,_ en - joy_ our fol - ly!
tut_to nel mon - do è bur_la,
Let us en_joy our fol - ly!
..... l'uom è na_to bur_lo - ne,
us en_joy_ our fol - ly!
tut - to, tut_to nel mon_do è bur_la,
Let us en joy,_ en_joy_ our fol - ly!
tut - to, tut_to nel mon_do è bur_la,
Let us en_joy,_ en - joy_ our fol - ly!
(60)
ff
pp

A
Q
EN
AL
N
M
Dr. C
FOR
B
P
- - - - - ti,
tut-ti gab-ba-ti, gab-ba-ti, gab-
- - - - ter,
Lean-er or fat-ter, we frol-ic and
ti
tut - - - - ti gab-ba -
see,
I - - - -dly we chat-
pp
tut - - - - - - - - to
pp Ah!
tut-ti gab-ba - - ti,
tut - - ti gab-
What does it mat - - ter,
what does it
pp
tut-to nel mon - do è
Let us en-joy our
marcato

pp
A
-ba-ti!
chat-ter!
tut
pp You
Q
-ti!
-ter!
tut - - - - ti.........
You see,
FEN
tut-ti gab-ba-ti, gabba-ti, gab - ba-ti!
Lean-er or fat-ter, it nev-er will mat-ter!
FAL
N
...... tutto nel mon - do è bur-la,
Let us en - joy our fol-ly!
M
-ba ti, tut-ti gab - ba
mat - ter, what does it mat - ter?
Dr. C
bur-la, è bur - la.................... tutto, tutto,
fol-ly, en-joy man and his fol-ly!
pp
FOR
tut-ti gab-ba-ti, gabba-ti, gab-
Lean-er-or-fat-ter,-we frol-ic-and
B
P
marcato
p

A
R
EN
AL
N
M
C
OR
B
P
- ti tut - ti gab - ba - ti...................... tutto nel mon - -
see, What does it mat - ter, Let us en - joy
...... tut - ti gab - ba - ti, gabba - ti, tutto nel mon - do è bur -
Lean - er or fat - ter no mat - ter, Let us en - joy our fol -
Ir - ri - de l'un l'al - tro o - gni mor - tal, tut - - to nel mon - do è
We chat - ter and flat - ter and gai - ly pre - tend. Let us en - joy our
tutto nel mon - do è
Let us en - joy our
tut - ti gab - ba - - - ti!
What does it mat - - - ter?
- - ti, tut - ti, tut - ti gab - ba - - ti!
Lean - er or fat - ter no mat - - ter!
tut - to è bur - - la,
What does it mat - - ter?
- ba - ti! Irri - de l'un l'al - tro o - gni mor - tal!
chat - ter But - what - does - it - mat - ter - We - laugh - in - the - end!
tutto nel mon - do è
Let us en - joy our

A
do è bur_la,
our fol_ly!
Q
_la, tut_to nel mon _ do è bur_la,
_ly! Let us en_joy our fol_ly!
FEN
bur_la, tut_to nel mon_do è bur _ la,
fol_ly! Let us en_joy our fol_ly! Ah!
FAL
bur_la, tut_to nel mon_do è bur _ la,
fol_ly! Let us en_joy our fol _ ly!
N
Tut_to nel mon _ _
Let us en_joy
M
Tut_to nel mon_do è bur _
Let us en_joy our fol _
Dr C
tut _ _ to nel mon_do è
Let us en_joy our
FOR
tut_to nel mon _ do è
Let us en_joy our
B
tut_to nel mon_do è bur _ la,
Let us en_joy our fol _ ly!
P
bur_la, tut_to nel mon_do è bur _ la,
fol_ly! Let us en_joy our fol _ ly!
tut_to nel mon _ do è
Let us en_joy our

A
Q
EN
AL
N
M
Dr. C
FOR
B
P
tut - to è bur - la, tut -
Laugh and let us be gay! You'll
tut-to nel mon - do è bur-la, tut-ti gab-
Let us en-joy our fol-ly! What does it
tut-to, tut-to nel mon - do è bur-la,
Laugh and let us en-joy our fol-ly!
tut-ti gab-ba
Lean-er or fat
do è bur-la.
our fol-ly!
la, tut-to nel mon - do è bur-la,
ly! Let us en-joy our fol-ly!
bur-la, tut-to nel mon-do è bur - la.
fol-ly! Let us en-joy our fol - ly!
bur-la, tut-to nel mon-do è bur - la,
fol-ly! Let us en-joy our fol - ly!
tut-to, tut-to nel mon - do è bur-la,
Laugh and let us en-joy our fol-ly!
tut-to nel mon-do è bur - la,
Let us en-joy our fol - ly!
tut-to nel mon - do è bur-la,
Let us en-joy our fol-ly!
tut-to nel mon-do è bur - la,
Let us en-joy our fol - ly!
bur-la, tut-to nel mon-do è bur - la,
fol-ly! Let us en-joy our fol - ly!
(61)

A
-ti tut-ti gab-ba - - ti!
see, what does it mat - - ter?
Q
-ba - - - - - - ti!
mat - - - - - - ter?
FEN
p
ir - ri - de l'un l'al-tro,
Yes. Fun is a tri-umph
FAL
-ti, gab-ba - - - - - ti!
-ter, no mat - - - - - ter!
N
p
tut - -
Let us
M
p
tut-ti gab-
What does it
D.r C
FOR
p
tut-ti gab-ba - - -
Lean-er or fat - - -
B
P

A
Q
TEN
FAL
N
M
C
FOR
B
P
Ir-ri - - de l'un
Yes, what does it
Ir-ri - - de l'un l'al - -
Yes, what does it mat - -
Tut-ti gab-ba - - - -
I-dly we chat - - - -
-ti tut-ti gabba - - ti!
laugh, what does it mat - - ter?
-ba - - - - - ti!
mat - - - - - ter?
Ir - - ri - de l'un l'al-tro
Oh! Let us be mer-ry
-ti, gab-ba - - - - - ti!
-ter no mat - - - - - ter!

A
l'al - - tro o - gni mor - tal,
mat - - ter be gay and pre - tend!
Q
- tro, l'un l'al - tro o-gni mor - tal,
- ter, be gay and let's all pre - tend!
FEN
ma ri-de ben chi
Fun is the fi - - nal
FAL
ti, ma ri-de ben, ri-de ben... chi
ter. Fun is the triumph of mind o-ver
N
ah! ah! ah!
Ha! Ha! Ha!
M
ah! ah! ah!
Ha! Ha! Ha!
Dr.C
ma ri-de ben chi
Fun is the fi - - nal
FOR
ma ri-de ben, ri-de ben... chi
Fun is the tri-umph of mind o-ver
B
ma ri-de ben chi
Fun is the fi - - nal
P
ma ri-de ben, ri-de ben... chi
Fun is the triumph of mind o-ver
ah! ah! ah!
Ha! Ha! Ha!
ah! ah! ah!
Ha! Ha! Ha!
ma ri-de ben chi
Fun is the fi - - nal
ma ri-de ben, ri-de ben... chi
Fun is the tri-umph of mind o-ver
(62)

A
Q
FEN
FAL
N
M
Dr C
FOR
B
P
ff
ma........ ri - de ben chi ri - de ah! ah! ah!
tri - umph - of mind o - ver mat-ter! Ha! Ha! Ha!
ma......... ri - de ben chi ri - de ah! ah! ah!
tri - - umph of mind o - ver mat-ter! Ha! Ha! Ha!
ri - de la ri - sata fi - nal,...................... ma ride ben chi
tri - umph if - you laugh in the end. Fun is the fi - nal
ri - de la ri - sa - ta fi - nal ma ride ben, ride ben chi
mat - ter if we laugh in - the end. Fun is the triumph of mind o-ver
ah!.. ah! ah! ah!
Ha! Ha! Ha! Ha!
ah!....... la ri - sa - ta fi - nal ah! ah! ah!
Ha! If - you laugh in - the end Ha! Ha! Ha!
ri - de la ri - sata fi - nal,...................... ma ride ben chi
tri - umph if - you laugh in the end. Fun is the fi - nal
ri - de la ri - sa - ta fi - nal, ma ride ben, ride ben chi
mat - ter if you laugh in the end. Fun is the triumph of mind o-ver
ri - de la ri - sata fi - nal,...................... ma ride ben chi
tri-umph if - you laugh in the end. Fun is the fi - nal
ri - de la ri - sa - ta fi - nal, ma ride ben, ride ben chi
mat - ter if you laugh in the end. Fun is the triumph of mind o-ver
ah!.. ah! ah! ah!
Ha! Ha! Ha! Ha!
ma ri - de ben chi ri - de ah! ah! ah!
Ha! If - you laugh in - the end. Ha! Ha! Ha!
ri - de la ri - sata fi - nal,...................... ma ride ben chi
tri-umph if - you laugh in the end. Fun is the fi - nal
ri - de la ri - sa - ta fi - nal, ma ride ben, ride ben chi
mat - ter if we laugh in the end. Fun is the triumph of mind o-ver
8

A
ah! ....
Ha!
ma ride ben, ride ben chi
Fun is the tri-umph of mind o-ver
Q
ma ride ben chi ri - de,
on-ly be sure to laugh in the end!
ma ride ben, ride ben chi
Fun is the tri-umph of mind o-ver
FEN
ri - de la ri-sata final, ...
tri-umph if you laugh in the end.
ma ride ben, ride ben chi
Fun is the tri-umph of mind o-ver
FAL
ri - de la ri-sa - ta fi - nal,
mat - ter, if we laugh in the end!
ma ride ben, ride ben chi
Fun is the tri-umph of mind o-ver
N
ah! la ri-sa - ta fi - nal,
Ha! If you laugh in the end!
M
ah! la ri-sa - ta fi - nal,
Ha! If you laugh in the end!
Dr C
ri - de la ri-sata final, ...
tri-umph if you laugh in the end!
FOR
ri - de la ri-sa - ta fi - nal,
mat - ter if you laugh in the end!
B
ri - de la ri-sata final, ...
tri-umph if you laugh in the end!
P
ri - de la ri-sa - ta fi - nal,
mat - ter if you laugh in the end!
ah! ....
Ha!
ma ride ben chi ri - de
tri - umph if you laugh in the end!
ri - de la ri-sata final, ...
tri - umph if you laugh in the end!
ri - de la ri-sa - ta fi - nal,
mat - ter if you laugh in the end!
mf

cres.
cres.
A
ri - de, ma ri_de ben, ri_de ben chi
ri - de la ri_sa - ta fi-
mat - ter, Fun is the tri-umph of mind o-ver
mat - ter If — we laugh — in — the
Q
ri - de, ma ri_de ben, ri_de ben chi
ri - de la ri_sa - ta fi-
mat - ter, Fun is the tri-umph of mind o-ver
mat - ter If — we laugh — in — the
TEN
ri - de, ma ri_de ben, ri_de ben chi
ri - de la ri_sa - ta fi-
mat - ter, Fun is the tri-umph of mind o-ver
mat - ter If — we laugh — in — the
FAL
ri - de, ma ri_de ben, ri_de ben chi
ri - de la ri_sa - ta fi-
mat - ter, Fun is the tri-umph of mind o-ver
mat - ter If — we laugh — in — the
N
ma ri_de ben, ri_de ben chi
ri - de la ri_sa - ta fi-
Fun is the tri-umph of mind o-ver
mat - ter If — we laugh — in — the
M
ma ri_de ben, ri_de ben chi
ri - de la ri_sa - ta fi-
Fun is the tri-umph of mind o-ver
mat - ter If — we laugh — in — the
Dr C
ma ri_de ben, ri_de ben chi
ri - de la ri_sa - ta fi-
Fun is the tri-umph of mind o-ver
mat - ter If — we laugh — in — the
FOR
ma ri_de ben, ri_de ben chi
ri - de la ri_sa - ta fi-
Fun is the tri-umph of mind o-ver
mat - ter If — we laugh — in — the
B
la ri_sa - ta fi-
If — we laugh — in — the
P
la ri_sa - ta fi-
If — we laugh — in — the
la ri_sa - ta fi-
If — we laugh — in — the
la ri_sa - ta fi-
If — we laugh — in — the
la ri_sa - ta fi-
If — we laugh — in — the
la ri_sa - ta fi-
If — we laugh — in — the
cres.
cres.

tronca
A
Q
FEN
FAL
N
M
Dr C
FOR
B
P
nal ah! ah! ah! ah!
end! Ha! Ha! Ha! Ha!
nal, ride ben chi ri-de la risa-ta fi-nal.
end! Yes, no mat-ter, you will win if you laugh in the end!
63

UN PO' PIÙ LENTO
I.º TEMPO
A
Q
FEN
FAL
N
M
D.r C
FOR
B
P
ah! ah! ah!
Ha, ha, ha!
Tut - ti gab - ba - ti!
What does it mat-ter?
tutti gab-
What does it
Tut - ti gab - ba - ti!
Lean - er or fat - ter,
tut-ti gabba - ti,
What does it mat-ter?
tut - ti gab - ba - ti!
cres.

A
Q
FEN
FAL
N
M
Dr. C
FOR
B
P
ah! ah! ah! ah! ah! ah!............... tutti gabba
Ha, ha, ha, ha, ha, ha! What does it mat-
ah! ah! ah! ah! ah! ah!............... tut_ti gabba
Ha, ha, ha, ha, ha, ha! What does it mat-
-ba_ti, tut_ti gabba_ti, tut_ti gab_ba_ti
mat-ter, What does it mat-ter, What does it mat-ter?
tut_ti gabba - ti, tut_ti gab_ba_ti
What does it mat - ter, What does it mat-ter?
ah! ah! ah! ah! ah! ah!............... tut_ti gabba
Ha, ha, ha, ha, ha, ha! What does it mat-
ah! ah! ah! ah! ah! ah!............... tut_ti gabba
Ha, ha, ha, ha, ha, ha! What does it mat-
-ba_ti, tut_ti gabba_ti, tut_ti gab_ba_ti
mat-ter, What does it mat-ter, What does it mat-ter?
tut_ti gabba - ti, tut ti gab_ba_ti
What does it mat - ter, What does it mat-ter?
-ba_ti, tut_ti gabba_ti, tut_ti gab_ba_ti
mat-ter, What does it mat-ter, What does it mat-ter?
tut_ti gabba - ti, tut_ti gab_ba_ti
What does it mat - ter, What does it mat-ter?
tut_ti gab_ba_ti, gabba
What does it matter, yes, mat-
tut_ti gab_ba_ti, gabba
What does it mat-ter, yes, mat-

A

- ti, ah!
- ter? Ah! ....

Q

- ti, tut-ti gab-ba-ti, gabba-ti, gab - ba - ti, tut-ti gabba - ti, tut-ti gab-
- ter? Lean-er or fat-ter we frol-ic and chat - ter, I-dly we chat - ter, frol- ic and

EN

tut-ti gab-ba-ti, gabba-ti, gab - ba - ti, tut-ti gabba - ti, tut-ti gab-
Lean-er or fat-ter we frol-ic and chat - ter, I - dly we chat - ter frol- ic and

AL

ah! ah! ah! ah! tut-ti tut-ti gabba-ti, gabba-ti, gab-
Ah! Ah! Ah! Lean-er or fat-ter we frol-ic and flat-ter and

N

- ti, ah!
- ter? Ah! ....

M

- ti, tut-ti gab-ba-ti, gabba-ti, gab - ba - ti, tut-ti gabba - ti, tut-ti gab-
- ter? Lean-er or fat - ter we frol-ic and chat - ter, I - dly we chat - ter, frol- ic and

C

tut-ti gab-ba-ti, gabba-ti, gab - ba - ti, tut-ti gabba - ti, tut-ti gab-
Lean-er or fat-ter we frol-ic and chat - ter I - dly we chat - ter frol- ic and

FOR

ah! ah! ah! ah! tut-ti tut-ti gabba-ti, gabba-ti, gab-
Ah! Ah! Ah! Lean-er or fat-ter we frol-ic and flat-ter and

B

tut-ti gab-ba-ti, gabba-ti, gab - ba - ti, tut-ti gabba - ti, tut-ti gab-
Lean-er or fat-ter we frol-ic and chat - ter, I - dly we chat - ter, frol- ic and

P

ah! ah! ah! ah! tutti tut-ti gabba-ti, gabba-ti, gab-
Ah! Ah! Ah! Lean-er or fat-ter we frol-ic and flat-ter and

- ti, tut-ti gab-ba-ti, gabba-ti, gab - ba - ti, tut-ti gab-ba - ti, tut-ti gab-
- ter? Lean-er or fat-ter we frol-ic and chat - ter, I - dly we chat - ter, frol- ic and

- ti, tut-ti gab-ba-ti, gabba-ti, gab - ba - ti, tut-ti gab-ba - ti, tut-ti gab-
- ter? Lean-er or fat-ter we frol-ic and chat - ter, I - dly we chat - ter, frol- ic and

tut-ti gab-ba-ti, gabba-ti, gab - ba - ti, tut-ti gab-ba - ti, tut-ti gab-
Lean-er or fat-ter we frol-ic and chat - ter, I - dly we chat - ter, frol- ic and

ah! ah! ah! ah! tut-ti tut-ti gab-ba-ti, gab-ba-ti, gab-
Ah! Ah! Ah! Lean - er or fat-ter we frol-ic and flat-ter and

A
Q
-ba - ti, tut-ti gab-ba - ti!
flat - ter, triumph of mind o-ver mat - ter!
FEN
-ba - ti, tut-ti gab-ba-ti, gab-ba - ti!
flat - ter, tri-umph of mind o-ver mat - ter!
FAL
-ba - ti, tut-ti gab-ba-ti, gab-ba - ti!
chat-ter, tri-umph of mind o-ver mat - ter.
N
M
-ba - ti, tut-ti gab-ba-ti, gab-ba - ti!
flat - ter, tri-umph of mind o-ver mat - ter!
Dr. C
-ba - ti, tut-ti gab-ba-ti, gab-ba - ti!
flat - ter, tri-umph of mind o-ver mat - ter!
FOR
-ba - ti, tut-ti gab-ba-ti, gab-ba - ti!
chat - ter, tri-umph of mind o-ver mat - ter!
B
-ba - ti, tut-ti gab-ba-ti, gab-ba - ti!
flat - ter, tri-umph of mind o-ver mat - ter!
P
-ba - ti, tut-ti gab-ba-ti, gab-ba - ti!
chat - ter, tri-umph of mind o-ver mat - ter!
ba - ti, tut-ti gab-ba-ti, gab-ba - ti!
flat - ter, tri-umph of mind o-ver mat - ter!
-ba - ti, tut-ti gab-ba-ti, gab-ba - ti!
flat - ter, tri-umph of mind o-ver mat - ter!
-ba - ti, tut-ti gab-ba-ti, gab-ba - ti!
flat - ter, tri-umph of mind o-ver mat - ter!
-ba - ti, tut-ti gab-ba-ti, gab-ba - ti!
chat-ter, tri-umph of mind o-ver mat - ter!
(64)
ff sempre

END OF OPERA